MARRIED BY MISTAKE!

BY
RENEE ROSZEL

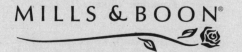

MILLS & BOON®

To Doug, my husband, with whom I've shared
more than half my life. I love you.

*First published in Great Britain 1998
Harlequin Mills & Boon Limited,
Eton House, 18-24 Paradise Road, Richmond, Surrey TW9 1SR*

© Renee Roszel Wilson 1998

ISBN 0 263 80724 X

*Set in Times Roman 10½ on 11¼ pt.
02-9803-54695 C1*

*Printed and bound in Great Britain
by Mackays of Chatham PLC, Chatham*

CHAPTER ONE

"LUCY, darling, what— Oh, Lord! Twins!"

Lucy frowned and stretched, then winced as pain stabbed through her hip. What an odd dream. Jack was in it, and he sounded so—so troubled. It wasn't like him to be troubled. He was an easygoing guy.

She felt another twinge in her hip, and her eyelids fluttered as she fought coming awake. She was so tired. Every fiber in her being cried out to be left alone. But something nagged at her brain, making her battle the urge to fall back to sleep.

As her eyes fully opened, she grimaced in confusion. Why was her head lolling on the seat cushion of an unfamiliar velvet sofa? And why were her legs cramped and twisted awkwardly on the cold, wood floor of—

She jerked up, shocked to discover that she'd dozed off. She couldn't believe she had actually fallen asleep in such a scary situation. Swiping at her eyes, she cleared away the blur of exhaustion. The flicker of two dwindling candles on a dust-coated end table was her only light, but enough to make it clear that her little sister was no longer sleeping on the sofa. Lucy had been comforting her, holding her hand. *But now, she was gone*! Lucy jumped to her feet, her heart going to her throat. "Helen?"

In the dimness she could see the newborn baby girls, still on the velvet cushion—such a small, precious bundle—swaddled in her raincoat. Thank heaven for that. Pulling her sweater tighter around her, she began to panic. It was freezing in the old D'Amour mansion, and her sister had just given birth, prematurely, to twins. She

5

was weak and cold, so where could she have gone?
"*Helen*!" When her only answer was silence, fright
clutched her by the throat. "*Helen*!" she cried in des-
peration. "Please—where are you?"

The sound of someone running filled her ears, and she
spun toward the den's entry in time to see a tall, dark
figure appear at the door, just beyond the reaches of the
candles' illumination. With the intruder's appearance,
her heart stopped with dread. What was happening? She
was so exhausted, so emotionally depleted, her eyes had
to be playing tricks on her. Or was she hallucinating?
Maybe, if she were very, very lucky, she was still asleep.
Yes! *Yes*, that had to be it! She was asleep, and this
massive, threatening figure was *not* there and Helen was
dozing peacefully on the couch beside her babies.

Balling her fists, Lucy squeezed her eyes tight, pleading, "*Please—please let me wake up from this nightmare!*"

Footfalls that sounded all too real advanced across the
gritty floorboards. Terror and helplessness surged
through her. All she could think of to do was to fling
herself across the babies in an effort to protect them.

As she was about to lunge toward the couch, she detected the most incongruous sound. A wry chuckle. At
that same instant, gentle hands gripped her upper arms.
"Lucy, Lucy..." Her name was spoken with soft ur-
gency, and she felt herself being shaken slightly. "I
know I'm not the man of your dreams, but a nightmare?
Give me a break."

That voice! She knew that voice! But it couldn't be
him. *Couldn't be Jack*. He was spending the month in
Bermuda. His last letter had been mailed from there.

She dropped her fists to her sides and opened her eyes.
The first sight she saw was a cinnamon brown gaze,
shimmering with melancholy humor. "Jack?" Though
the candles were flickering low, their light feeble, she

could never mistake those eyes. "Jack!" She grabbed at his shirtfront. "Oh, thank heavens you're here. Helen's missing. You have to help me find—"

"Calm down." He pulled her into his arms. "I've already carried Helen to the car and notified Skaggs Hospital that we're coming."

So relieved she couldn't find words, she hugged him with all her strength. "What—what are you doing in Branson?"

"Oh, the usual." He held her close, his breath warm against her hair. "You know. Slaying dragons. Rescuing damsels in distress."

She relished the harbor of his embrace and the comforting sound of his voice more than she could have imagined. Unfortunatcly, before she was ready to relinquish him, he stepped away. With a nod, he indicated the couch where Lucy's infant nieces were lying, wide-eyed, in their makeshift bedding. "What do you say we rescue these little damsels?"

She didn't know how Jack managed it, but she actually felt good enough to smile.

She shivered. The mild March day had turned mean and cold around midnight. The worst possible timing, considering everything.

He must have seen her tremor, for he shrugged off his suit coat and draped it about her shoulders. His body warmth hovered in the fabric along with his pleasant, familiar scent. Gratefully, she slid her arms into the sleeves, hugging herself. The expensive garment swallowed her all the way past her fingertips, but she didn't care. She couldn't remember when she'd needed warmth so badly.

When she looked at him again, he had lifted the babies in his arms and turned to go. She scurried after him toward the front entrance. For some reason, she recalled her odd, coincidental dream about Jack and couldn't help but ask, "Did you call me darling in there?"

She thought she saw a slight hesitation in his step, then a sharp glance her way, but couldn't be sure, even under the full moon. He began to lope down the steps, his chuckle rumbling through the night. "Sure," he said. "I call all you Crosby girls darling. It keeps me from having to remember your names."

She flushed, feeling ridiculous, and followed him down. "Sorry. I guess I was a little hysterical."

"Forget it." He settled the twins into Helen's open arms, then helped Lucy into the back seat of his luxury rental car. She was startled when he leaned inside. His expression serious, he reached out, smoothing a strand of her blond hair behind her ear. "By the way, happy birthday, Luce."

He'd ducked out and was in the driver's seat before she could react. As he started the engine, she smiled shyly, focusing on her knees. She should have realized Jack wouldn't forget.

One of the babies whimpered, and Lucy's gaze shot to her little sister. "Helen? Is everything okay?"

The new mother glanced over her shoulder and smiled. Though she looked tired, her expression was happy. "In such good hands as yours and Jack's, how could anything be wrong?"

Suddenly, Lucy found herself battling down an urge to burst into tears. It wasn't until this moment—when the crisis was over—that she realized how out-of-her-mind stressed she'd been. Thank goodness the births had been normal.

Jack lifted the receiver of his car phone. "I'll call the Branson police. Elissa went there to report you two missing." When he hung up, he relayed the message that Elissa would meet them at the hospital.

Lucy sagged into the plush leather, grateful that Jack was here, handling everything.

A dark thought intruded—the other thing—the *Stadler* thing—and she bit her lip hard, preferring pain to remembering. This was no time to think nasty, bitter thoughts about heartbreak and betrayal. This was a time for positive thinking. Her glance shifted to Jack's wide shoulders, then slid forward to scan his long, tanned fingers, curled around the steering wheel. Yes, Jack was a positive subject. She would think about Jack.

Jack had been their stepbrother fifteen years ago. Though he'd only lived in her father's home for three years, and his mother, Rita Gallagher, had never allowed her dad to adopt him, the Crosby girls had refused to divorce Jack, even when his mother ran off with another man. Though he wasn't truly a relative, he was very dear to them.

As he chewed up the ten miles to the hospital, Lucy found herself wondering how it was that he seemed to sense when the Crosby sisters needed him.

She marveled that he always seemed to be there.

Lucy accepted the paper cup of vending-machine coffee that Jack handed her. The Skaggs maternity wing was located in the newest hospital addition. Its waiting room was typical of waiting rooms everywhere, unadorned, antiseptic. The alcove was painted in restful hues of turquoise and mauve, with footstep-muffling carpet that seemed unnecessary in the predawn silence.

The furniture consisted of blond, wooden chairs butted armrest to armrest against the walls, the thinly padded seats of dark turquoise only comfortable enough for the most weary human being. But Lucy had no intention of going anywhere. She was that tired and that emotionally drained.

Yet she was also grateful. The doctor had reported that Helen and the babies were going to be fine.

"Where's Elissa?" Jack sat down in the chair on her left.

"Oh, you know Elissa. She's pacing somewhere."

"That's our Elissa. Little mother hen." He placed a casual arm behind her. "How are you doing?"

She knew he was referring to Stadler, but she didn't want to talk about that. The pain of his rejection was too raw, too new. Taking a stalling sip of the burning drink he'd brought her, she nodded. "I'm great. Now that I know Helen and the babies are no worse for the wear."

"You did a good job." He grinned down at her. The same, wonderful grin she'd found so comforting when she'd been a timid little girl, afraid of storms, creaking boards and barking dogs. Almost everything, really. Then big, strong Jack had come into their lives, apparently fearing nothing. Seven years her senior, he'd seemed quite grown-up when she'd been eight and he'd been fifteen. "You were smart to put that candle in the window, Luce."

She couldn't help but return his smile, though her effort was weak. His scent wafted around her, familiar and welcome. "Thanks. I had no idea you'd be the answer to my prayer."

An enigmatic, almost pained, expression fleeted across his features. Lucy couldn't imagine why, but whatever it meant, it was quickly gone. Probably fatigue. They were all reeling with exhaustion.

He cleared his throat. "So, you and your nieces share a birthday."

She hadn't thought of that. "I guess we do." Her laughter bubbled, but lacked much humor. A yawn threatened and she covered her mouth with a hand. Peering up at the man beside her, she shook her head. "Sorry. It's been a long night."

His smile, this time, was less visible. "Extremely. I got to the inn around midnight, after driving from the Springfield airport. When Elissa went to find you and Helen to tell you I was there, she discovered you'd never returned from your walk. We drove around looking for two hours before we split up and she went to the police station. That's when I saw the candle in the mansion window."

"It was an afterthought. Helen couldn't be left alone. The second baby took her own sweet time deciding to be born. I had to do something."

There was a long pause, and Lucy felt a little uncomfortable, unsure why. "Elissa told me about Stadler," he finally said. "If you want, we can talk about it."

At the reminder, her muscles tensed and her heart constricted. All she could do was shake her head. She supposed she'd known the subject would have to come up. After a few strained moments, she managed, "I can't." Jack's face was blurry and she blinked her vision clear. "Not yet. But thanks."

"No problem." His jaw clenched and unclenched. "I can wait." He pursed his lips as though working to change the subject, bless him. "Where's Damien?"

Grateful to have something else to think about, Lucy sighed. "He's in the Denver airport, snowed in. His book tour is just about over. Two more cities." She took another sip of coffee, then smiled with recollection. "When I talked to him a half hour ago, he pretty much said the tour was *over* as far as he was concerned. To quote him, he said, 'I don't care if my book is number one on the *New York Times* bestseller's list and my publisher drops dead from apoplexy. I'm damned sure going to be with Helen and my baby girls as soon as this snow lets up!'" She was happy for her little sister and the staunch supporter she had in her husband. "Damien's a wonderful guy."

She noticed that Jack was looking at her in his direct, serious way. His vivid gaze was contemplative. She took a quiet minute to stare back, filling her eyes and her heart with him. It was awfully good to have him there.

His thick brown hair tapered tidily to his starched white collar. His silk tie was loosened at the neck, making him look less like a successful restaurateur and more like the teenage rebel she'd first known.

He'd rolled up his shirtsleeves, exposing sturdy forearms. Strong, protective arms that had lifted her out of a tree when she'd gotten herself stuck. Arms that had held her down so that the doctor could stitch up a gash in her thigh after she'd fallen off her bike. She bit her lip at the memory of how she'd shouted at him, telling him she hated him and would despise him forever. Of course she hadn't meant a word of it. He'd laughed at her, telling her she was crazy for him and she knew it.

She half smiled at the memory. She'd had a terrific crush on him back then. She supposed she hadn't hidden it well. Running a restless hand through her eternally tousled hair, she had an urge to snuggle in his arms the way she had when she'd been a frightened child. She needed some good, old-fashioned comforting.

"The babies weren't due until April, right?"

His question pulled her from her musing, and she flushed, wondering if he would be embarrassed to know she'd been thinking about his arms, of all things. She nodded. "April second. Two more weeks." Her heart twisted and she had to blink back guilty tears. "Oh, Jack—the whole thing was my fault."

He chuckled, showing a flash of teeth. "*You* got Helen pregnant?"

She did a double take, then couldn't help but laugh at his joke. "Jack, your restaurants keep you too busy. You need to take a course in human sexuality." She shook her head in mock incredulity, but felt less depressed because of his teasing. Still, as her thoughts returned to the events of the night, her buoyant mood faded. "Really, if I hadn't been so—so upset, Helen wouldn't have suggested we take a walk and we wouldn't have been in the middle of nowhere when she went into labor."

"Sometimes twins come early, I understand. Don't blame yourself."

She glanced at him again, and this time when her lips twitched upward, there was wistful gratitude there. "Did you take a course?"

A dark eyebrow rose. "You just told me I needed to."

"Not that course." She slipped into the crook of his arm, yawning again. "Another course—where you learned all the right things to say."

His pleasant chuckle reverberated through her. Very vaguely, she sensed her coffee cup being lifted from her fingers as overwhelming exhaustion and Jack's snug closeness ushered her into the land of Nod.

Lucy, Jack and Elissa visited Helen that afternoon after everybody had had a little rest. Just as visiting hours were ending, Damien Lord dashed in, rumpled, unshaven, the image of a man possessed. Lucy smiled at him as he rushed by. He was such a handsome man, eye patch, scars and all.

"Darling." He took Helen in his arms. "You look wonderful."

Helen kissed Damien long and lovingly, her arms tight about his shoulders. When the kiss ended and Damien drew away enough to look at her, she held his face between her hands. "You look tired, honey."

He grinned, relief etched on his face, then kissed the tip of her nose. "I just became a father. It takes a lot out of you."

"No kidding." Helen slipped her arms around his

neck again. "Well, since you're in such a delicate con-
dition, maybe you'd better lie down beside me and rest."

Jack cleared his throat and stood. "Sounds like our
cue to leave, ladies."

Damien turned, finally acknowledging them with a
wave and a striking smile.

Elissa got up from her chair and smoothed the wrin-
kles from her wool skirt. "Well, I know I should get
back. Jule's become a great right hand for me at the inn,
but I think I've left her alone long enough for one day."

"We'll see you tomorrow, Helen." Lucy approached
her sister and squeezed her fingers. Bending forward, she
kissed her brother-in-law's whisker-roughened jaw.
"You get some rest, too—Daddy."

Helen took hold of her sister's hand and turned toward
Jack and Elissa. "You two go on and get the car. I need
a second with Lucy."

Jack slipped an arm around Elissa's shoulders and led
her from the room. "It must be a secret club, and we
don't know the handshake."

"Well, when we start our own secret club, they'll be
sorry," Elissa said with a laugh.

After they were gone and the door closed, Helen released Damien and indicated the opposite side of the bed
with a pat. "Sit here, honey. I need to talk to my sister
for a minute."

Lucy felt embarrassed and shy. "Look, Helen, you've
already thanked me for helping you with the babies. But
it was my fault we were out there—"

"Hush!" Helen touched Lucy's mouth with her fingertips. "I suggested the walk. I flew from New York
against Damien's wishes and the doctor's orders, so
enough about fault. We're fine, and we're here to celebrate a whole bunch of birthdays, and…" Helen's expression grew sly. "And one other important and wonderful event!"

Lucy grew confused. She looked at Damien who appeared equally puzzled, though he smiled. "I don't know what she's talking about, either, but…" He took Lucy's hand and lifted it to his lips, brushing a kiss across her knuckles. "How can I repay you for saving Helen and my little girls?"

His expression was so full of emotion, Lucy's eyes filled with tears. Pulling her lips between her teeth, she swallowed to get control of her voice. "I'm glad…" The words were so weak and shuddering, she stopped, trying again. "I'm glad everything turned out okay."

"Now don't make me cry, you two. It hurts," Helen interrupted, sounding a little quivery herself. "Will you let me say something that's *very* important?" She propped herself up on her pillows to have better eye contact with her sister. After getting comfortable, she took both of Lucy's hands in hers. "Do you realize you've fulfilled *all* the requirements of the myth?"

Lucy was baffled. She looked at Damien in time to see his expression change from soft concern to wariness. "What are you saying, sweetheart?" He touched Helen's hair, smoothing it along the pillow.

His wife glanced at him, her expression loving. "The D'Amour myth." She returned her gaze to Lucy, her features animated. "You're going to marry Jack."

Lucy had never been so completely blindsided in her life. Not even by Stadler's appalling letter yesterday, telling her he was breaking their two-year engagement to marry someone else. After she'd waited a year, then nine more lonely months while the Shakespearean troupe extended their tour of Australia again and again. She had been devastated by Stadler's cruel blow. But this? This was *insane*!

She frowned, unable to do more than stare at her sister, who was obviously having a psychotic reaction to childbirth. Pulling a hand from Helen's grip, she felt her sister's forehead. "This isn't good."

"Is she feverish?" Worry edged Damien's voice.

"I'm afraid not." Lucy reached for the nurse's call button. "And talking crazy like she is, she should be burning up."

"I'm perfectly fine." Helen grabbed Lucy's wrist before she could call the nurses' station. "Don't you remember the myth?"

Lucy squinted down at her sister. "That—that thing about the birthday and the full moon?"

Helen nodded. "And sleeping in the mansion. And for your information, today is your birthday. Last night there was a full moon, and I know you slept because I saw you."

Wide-eyed, Lucy looked to Damien for guidance. "What should we do?"

"I don't know about you—" he grinned at his confused sister-in-law "—but when the time comes, I intend to kiss the bride."

Lucy's mind tumbled and skidded. Clearly, whatever psychosis that was affecting Helen had spread to her husband. She pulled from Helen's grasp and backed away. "If this is a joke, I'm not laughing."

Helen sat up, then grimaced, lying back down. "It's not a joke. Tell her, Damien." Taking the hand that had been stroking her hair, she kissed his palm. "Tell her that Jack Gallagher is her destiny, just like you were mine."

Damien lifted one shoulder in an offhand shrug, looking terribly charming—such a big man perched carefully on the small bed beside the woman he loved. Two unlikely people who had found each other in an improbable place, their chance meeting changing both their lives drastically. "I like Jack. You two would be a great couple," he said with a grin.

"But—but Jack's been like a brother to us," Lucy cried. "He—he…" She clamped her jaw. This conversation was ridiculous. "Besides, I—I can't conceive of marriage right now!" Her heart wanted to scream that concepts like "trust" and "commitment" were sour, bitter lies as far as she was concerned. Stadler's treachery had done great damage to her heart, damage not quickly mended—if ever.

Even so, Lucy wasn't the sort of person to get angry and shout or argue. She'd always been the peacemaker of the three sisters. So from long years of practice, she straightened her face. She wasn't mad at Helen. The sweet, stubborn dear had insisted on flying from New York just to be with Lucy on her birthday.

Clamping her hands together, she eyed them both with as much poise as she could muster. "I think the way you two met was extremely romantic, and it was a beautiful coincidence—considering the myth and all. But don't you breathe a word of that nonsense again or I'll—I'll…"

"What?" Helen asked with a smirk. "Knit me a really ugly sweater?" She laughed, then winced, but quickly regained her smile. "To be honest, it won't be necessary for either of us to lift a finger. Your fate is sealed."

Lucy's brows knit further and she stared pointedly at Damien. "The subject ends here, *right*?"

He winked. "I always said Jack was a damn lucky man. I just didn't know how lucky."

Lucy's lips parted in stunned disbelief. "You two are crazy."

"We are cute, aren't we?" Helen snuggled against her husband. "And we're happy for you, Lucy."

She drew a deep breath and forbade herself to tremble. "Get some sleep, both of you. You'll feel better tomorrow."

''You're cute when you're in denial,'' Helen said, waving goodbye. ''Now go away. Damien has some serious kissing to do.''

His low chuckle mingled with his wife's laughter, chasing Lucy from the room. As she scurried along the hallway toward the parking lot, she vowed that Jack would never get wind of what had been predicted today. Jack Gallagher felt indebted to their father for helping turn his life around, and because of that deep affection and appreciation, he cared for all three of the Crosby daughters—equally.

She would never allow him to be embarrassed by such a crazy notion!

Since Old Man Winter had decided to revisit Branson, Jack lit a fire in the inn's parlor. Luckily, March was not one of the busiest tourist months in the bustling Missouri town referred to as the ''Las Vegas of the Ozarks,'' so there was a vacant room for Jack.

Lucy had taken a long nap and a relaxing bath that afternoon, so she felt more human as she sat on the white muslin sofa, toying with the fringe of one of the colorful throw pillows. Covertly, she watched Jack as he and Elissa played gin on the Oriental rug before the fire.

Elissa slapped his hand as he picked up a card she'd just thrown on the discard pile. ''That's the third card of mine you've taken!''

He slipped it into his fan of cards. ''Can I help it if you don't know a good card when you see one?''

''You'd better take care,'' Elissa warned him, drawing another card. She frowned at it, scanned Jack with narrowed, suspicious eyes, then slapped it onto the discard pile. He plucked it up, and this time, Elissa dropped her cards and grabbed his hand with both of hers. ''Oh, no! Oh, no! There's a rule that you can't take more than three discards in a row.''

"Show me in the rule book." He laughed as she yanked on the playing card.

"Don't you trust me?" she squealed.

"Not a chance."

The card was now bent and twisted, but Jack didn't release it, only chuckled at Elissa's futile struggles as he placed it with his other cards.

"If you gin, I'll kill you."

"Gin," he said without missing a beat, his grin so delightfully devilish it stole Lucy's breath.

With a wild groan, Elissa yanked his cards from his fingers and tossed them into the air. "I will not play with a *cheater*!"

Lucy found herself joining the laugher. She reached out and caught a card as it fluttered down. "Jack, when will you learn that Elissa hates to lose?"

He glanced up at her. The firelight did clever things to his hair, giving him a bronze halo. His teeth seemed excessively white as he grinned her way. "Then you play with me. My health insurance rates will go down."

"Oh, you…" Elissa leaned over and tweaked his cleft chin. "You're the only man on earth I can't beat at gin and I hate that about you. It's an unforgivable flaw in your character."

He quirked an eyebrow at her. "That makes two unforgivable flaws. Lucy says I don't have a clue where babies come from."

"Really?" Elissa passed a dubious glance toward Lucy. "Do you suppose that supermodel who stalked him for six months thought that, too?"

"She didn't stalk me," Jack cut in, amusement in his voice. "She just followed me around and hid in my grounds from time to time."

Elissa stood. "Well, excuse me. I'm insane for suggesting she *stalked* you. After all, stalking is when somebody follows you around and hides in your grounds. My mistake.''

"Okay, okay. But she's safely back in France now," he said. "Getting treatment."

Elissa smiled playfully. "What was it she couldn't resist about you, Jack dear? Your gin game?"

Lucy's cheeks grew hot. "I was kidding when I said that, Elissa. I'm sure Jack is well aware of sexual— stuff."

Elissa laughed. "Lucy, Jack knew *stuff* even before his mother married Dad and they moved in with us." She gave him a superior smirk. "I should know because my room was right below his. I saw his girlfriends climbing up the trellis to his room."

Jack's expression grew sheepish, captivatingly so. "Hell. You knew?"

"*No!*" Lucy cried. "I don't believe it. I never saw any girls. And I ran in and jumped right into Jack's bed during thunderstorms."

"During thunderstorms the windows were closed," Elissa reminded her with a laugh.

The fire popped and hissed, and Jack turned away to look into the flames. Lucy had a feeling he was embarrassed about this discussion of his wild youth.

"On those infrequent nights when his window was closed, it kept out the rain *and* half the pubescent females in Kansas City." Elissa crossed her arms before her, eyeing Lucy as though she were a touch feeble-witted. "And you said he didn't know where babies came from. Just another example that you're not a good judge of men."

The remark was like a punch in her heart, and Lucy grimaced.

Suddenly, Elissa was standing before her, holding her face. "Gosh, I'm sorry. That wasn't—I didn't mean to— I was *trying* to be funny." She let out a disgusted breath and eyed the ceiling. "I'm just so furious at Stadler. That's all. Can you forgive me?"

Lucy swallowed to ease the lump of emotion that had formed in her throat, then nodded. "Sure—sure…"

"Hey." Elissa inhaled, clearly trying to lighten the mood. "How about some tea? Since you won't let us celebrate your birthday until Helen and the twins are home, we might as well have a cup of English Apple to commemorate year number twenty-six. What do you say?"

Lucy nodded. "Sounds good." She managed to smile and even make direct eye contact with her sister, who looked so upset by her slip of the tongue that Lucy couldn't be angry with her.

"Want some help?" Jack asked.

"No." Elissa faced him, thumping her fists on her hips. "Cardsharps must clean up the mess."

"I presume that's straight out of 'Elissa's Gin Rule Book for Sleazoids Who Beat Her'?"

"Chapter one." She lifted her chin in haughty affront. "Sleazoid."

After Elissa left the room, Lucy discovered that Jack was silently watching her. He bent one knee, curling an arm around it. "Would you like to play with me?"

She felt a strange tremor along her spine and shook it off. Helen's prediction that afternoon had left its lingering effect, and Jack's innocent question seemed erotic. Shaking her head, she sat farther back in the fluffy couch, clutching the pillow she'd been toying with to her breasts. "Oh—no, I'm not very good at gin."

"Neither is Elissa." His grin was so appealing she found herself smiling back. "You tell her I said that and you're toast."

She nodded. "I know."

They watched each other for another minute before Jack tilted his head in a way that told her he was there to listen if she wanted to talk. It was bizarre how he could communicate so much without a word. No doubt it was because she knew him so well.

She shook her head. "I don't think you can help me with this, Jack."

"I could try."

Uncomfortable under his close scrutiny, she cleared her throat. "Just be my friend. Okay?"

Pursing his lips, he nodded. "Right."

He began to pick up the cards and she scanned him as he moved. Watched the energy of his actions, his economy of motion. The clothes he wore were simple, but rich. His beige trousers emphasized hard thighs and taut hips. His shirt was an emerald green knit, and as he moved, muscle rippled, making a tantalizing show of shoulders and arms. She lounged her head back, casually gazing, almost feasting. It was surprising how the simple act of gathering a few cast-off playing cards could be such eye candy.

His knuckle scraped against her ankle as he retrieved the last fallen card, and she yelped, not aware that she'd slipped into a daydream.

"Sorry." He came up beside her and sat on the couch to shuffle the cards. The broken one flipped out of the pack and landed in her lap. She gasped and flinched. "Aren't we a little jumpy tonight?" As he picked up the playing card, his fingers grazed her inner thigh through her trousers. Her body registered his brief touch with a queer tingling. "You seem nervous, Luce."

Restive, she tossed aside the pillow she'd been clutching, then thought better of it, squeezing it against her breasts as some sort of blue damask barrier. "No—no, I'm not nervous," she lied, then wondered why in the world she was. She and Jack were about as close as any man and woman could be who weren't really brother and sister. She avoided his scrutinizing gaze, focusing on his chin, deeply cleft and tan. Casting around for a safe topic, she asked, "Why are you in town, Jack?"

"I thought Elissa told you. I'm thinking of opening my fifth Gallagher's Bistro here in Branson." She met his eyes, not realizing she'd done so until his half-mast glance was sparkling into hers. "I figured what's good enough for New York City, Chicago, L.A. and London is good enough for the Crosby girls."

She smiled against her will. Suddenly shy, she scanned her lap to avoid his intense eyes. "Speaking on behalf of all the Crosby girls—I thank you."

"It's nothing." His hard thigh brushed hers as he relaxed back. "Nice fire."

"Bragging?" She was surprised to find herself ribbing *him* for a change.

He chuckled. "I'm almost as good at fire building as I am at playing gin." He nudged her with his elbow. "Sort of a Jack-of-all-trades."

She groaned. "That pun never gets any better."

He shrugged and she felt it. He was sitting very close. Which was fine. She had nothing to fear from him. Just because Helen said she and Jack were going to be married didn't mean Jack had amorous intentions toward her. And that was absolutely for the best, since the *last* thing on her mind was romance.

"Tired?"

"No." She shook her head, leaning against his shoulder. It was true. She wasn't tired, just downhearted, lost, emotionally adrift. Sleep seemed like the best escape, and her body was willing to oblige.

"Elissa's fixing your birthday tea."

"I'm awake."

He shifted to put his arm around her. "Sure you are, Luce."

She didn't know how long she napped in Jack's embrace before the doorbell woke her.

"I'll get it," Elissa said.

"Just in time," Jack murmured against her hair. "You didn't fall asleep, did you?"

"No…um—no—I'm *wide*…" She pushed away from him, her denial thick and slurred. When she straightened and looked around, she noticed a silver tea tray sitting on the coffee table.

He laughed softly. "You're not that wide."

She peered at him, fuzzy-headed. "What?"

His grin crooked, he started to say something, but Elissa interrupted. "Lucy, a telegram for you." She shifted toward the parlor entrance as Elissa breezed in, waving the yellow paper. Disquiet marred her lovely features. "Maybe Stadler's had a change of heart and has decided to crawl back."

Lucy took the telegram and tore it open. "You don't have to be so unhappy about the idea."

Elissa sat down in the leather chair beside the couch, worriedly eyeing her sister. "Well, before this English Apple turns to ice, I guess I'll go ahead and pour." She picked up a cup and the pot.

Lucy scanned the message, unable to believe her eyes. She had just read it a second time when a keening cry tore through the quiet and she felt faint. Somewhere, she heard the sound of a teacup breaking and splintering into pieces.

"Lucy!" Powerful male arms came around her, keeping her from slipping to the floor. "You screamed. What's happened?"

CHAPTER TWO

LUCY was dismayed with herself. She'd never fainted in her life. But this news was so awful. A shiver ran through her, bringing her fully back to consciousness.

When she realized Jack held her in his arms and was laying her on the couch, she let out a moan of embarrassment and pushed at his chest. "Oh—oh, I'm okay. Don't—don't…"

"Shush," he admonished. "You're as white as a ghost."

"Oh, Lord!" Elissa cried. From her angry tone, Lucy knew her sister was reading the telegram that had tumbled to the floor. "That *pig*! That putrefying slab of pork! He's coming *here*!"

Jack's worried glance lifted to Elissa although he didn't rise. With one hand on Lucy's shoulder, he remained kneeling beside her. "Who's coming here?"

Even in the dim light, Elissa's green eyes were blazing, her expression murderous. With an angry flourish, she thrust the telegram at Jack. "You read it. I'm afraid some more unattractive words will slip out of my mouth if I explain."

Jack looked confused as he took the telegram. With shaky fingers, Lucy reached for it. "Don't…" He evaded her attempt to snatch it from him. She groaned, covering her face with unsteady hands. She had to leave town immediately. But where could she go? They didn't have relatives anywhere. That didn't matter. She couldn't stay. *Not now.*

There was absolute quiet in the room for such a long time she had to peek through her fingers to see what was

25

going on. The world was blurry and she blinked, focusing on Jack as he stared at the telegram, his expression grim. When his glance caught Lucy's, something raw and violent flashed in his eyes. "Who does this piece of crap think he is?"

Lowering his glance to the page again, he gritted out the written words.

> "'Dearest Lucy,
> I know my letter must have come as a shock, and I apologize. After thinking about it, I know it is my duty to see you face-to-face and smooth things over.
> "'By the time you receive this, my fiancée and I will be winging our way to Branson, arriving on March 20. The first day of spring. Appropriate for my mission, for I've decided we must begin again. As great chums.
> "'You must meet my fiancée. You are both lovely, compliant women, and you will become fast friends. I know from your gentle temperament that you will agree that life is too short to harbor hard feelings between two people so sublimely simpatico as we two.
> Yours forever,
> Stadler'"

Jack made a guttural sound that sounded suspiciously like a curse. "That egotistical jackass." When he lifted his gaze to Lucy's face, his cinnamon eyes held a blaze that had nothing to do with the fire in the hearth. "I'll show him a brand of simpatico he won't find quite so sublime."

Lucy touched his arm. She appreciated his anger on her behalf, but shook her head. "You mustn't get involved, Jack." She struggled up on her elbows. "Besides, I don't plan to be here when he arrives."

"What?" Elissa bent over her sister. "Where are you going?"

Lucy ran a trembly hand through her hair. "I don't know. But I can't be here. I couldn't face him and—and his *new* fiancée. Surely you understand that."

Elissa straightened to her full five foot seven, looking offended. "I understand nothing of the kind." Plopping her fists on slender hips, she glowered at her sister. "You're going to meet him at the door with a two-by-four and pound him into dust. That's what you're going to do."

Lucy grimaced, slipping her legs over the side of the couch and coming up to sit. As she did, Jack seated himself beside her, his expression compassionate, his eyes telegraphing concern. "You'd leave before the twins and Helen are even out of the hospital? When she came all this way to be with you for your birthday?"

Lucy flinched at the reminder. It would be cruel to leave, abandoning Helen and the babies when her sister had come especially to see her. But what else could she do? She wasn't an aggressive person, loving a fight like her ex-lawyer sister, Elissa. Lucy hated confrontations, had spent her life trying to keep everyone calm and happy. People had always called her the sensitive one, the conciliatory one—"the sweet sister." Confrontation wasn't part of her character.

There was no way she could face Stadler and his new love. She shuddered at the thought, unable to look at either Elissa or Jack. "I can't stay." With her forlorn sigh, Jack took her hands in his big, warm ones, but she pulled away from his touch, too upset with her sniveling cowardice to allow herself to be comforted. "I—I'll go pack."

"No, you won't," Elissa warned. Lucy rose to her feet, but her older sister's hands clamped down on her shoulders, halting her. "You're not bolting like a jackrabbit, young lady. If you go, there will be nobody here to keep me from leaping on Stadler's back and strangling him. Do you want that? Do you want me to spend my best years behind bars just because I dispatched a worthless toad to Worthless-Toad Hell?''

Lucy winced, not so much from her sister's empty threat, but from the pressure of her blunt fingernails biting into her flesh. "Elissa, please don't belabor this. I'm leaving." She ducked out of her grasp. "Besides, I know you're itching to tell him off yourself."

"What I'm itching to do is beside the point." She took Lucy's face between her palms, forcing her to look into determined green eyes. "It's what *you* must do that we're talking about."

Tears welled and Lucy blinked them back. "I—I can't."

With a frown furrowing her brow, Elissa dropped her arms to her sides. "*Coward*!"

Lucy fought to keep from trembling. "Don't be mean, Elissa," she whispered.

There was movement beside her and she knew Jack had stood. "Your sister's right, Luce. Don't run away. Stay and show the jerk you don't care a damn about him."

Gulping around a knot of tears, Lucy faced him. "But—but I do care."

There was a brief slitting of his eyes, a fleeting sideways stirring of his jaw, an odd reaction. Almost as though he'd been slapped. The expression lasted only a millisecond before he offered a sympathetic smile. "Luce, the man has a tremendous ego, thinking his two women must meet. Hell, he probably has visions of a catfight over him right here in the parlor. The only thing he could hope for that could be more flattering than that would be if you ran." He reached out as though he was going to touch her cheek, then seemed to think better of it. With a slow fisting of his hand, he dropped it to his side. "Don't you have the smallest desire to avenge yourself for what he did to you?"

She stared, confused. "Avenge myself?"

"Great idea!" Elissa clapped her hands together with enthusiasm. "Make him think you're so bored to see him you can hardly remember his name." She sat down on the leather chair as Lucy pivoted to look at her. There was a frightening gleam in her older sister's eyes. "Now, Jack," Elissa was saying, "since Lucy's so rotten at plotting revenge, it's up to us. What would make Stadler hang by his thumbs, twisting in the wind, screaming in agony?"

Lucy sank to the sofa. What was going on? Her mind was too numbed to grasp what they were plotting. But it didn't really matter what they were talking about. She only needed another minute to get her strength back and she would tell them to forget it, then she'd go to her room and pack a bag and be gone.

"Being a man, I know what would put a gaping hole in my ego."

"What?" Elissa sat forward, expectancy stamped on her pretty face. "I hope it involves a 'kick me' sign on Stadler's back."

Jack grinned wryly. "Psychologically, yes."

"Please, you two, I—"

"Hush, sweetie!" Elissa waved a dismissal. "Jack has an idea."

Lucy shifted to stare at him, afraid she wasn't going to be thrilled by his idea—if it had anything to do with being in town when Stadler got here. She was sorry to have to admit it, even to herself, but she was as terrified of facing her ex-fiancé and his lady love as she had been of thunderstorms when she was a child.

She watched Jack's face. He surveyed her gently, his eyes narrowed with worry or possibly pity. She couldn't

be sure which, and squirmed. She didn't want Jack's
pity! She'd never thought about it until this minute, but
for some reason, she couldn't bear the idea of Jack's
feeling sorry for her. She wanted him to smile his teasing
smile, not watch her solemnly, his eyes stricken. Unable
to deal with what she saw and how that sight made her
feel, she twisted away.

Her uneasy movement seemed to affect him, and he
cleared his throat. "Okay, how's this for an idea? His
ego would be exploded all to hell if you met him with
a fiancé of your own."

Elissa's gasp drew Lucy's gaze. She felt dull-witted,
her brain trying to assimilate what Jack had said. But
apparently, Elissa's brain had readily grasped the con-
cept, deduced that it was perfect and ordered up a vic-
torious smile.

"Wonderful!" Elissa cried. "Fight fire with fire!
Make him think you've been as disloyal to him as he
was to you, the bag of dirt!" She vaulted up, clearly
deciding the plan was settled. "I can't wait to see his
face when he realizes you don't care a crumb for him!"

Lucy frowned at her sister, her astonished glance skit-
tering to Jack. She couldn't even express what she was
thinking. For instance, even if she agreed to this, just
who would be her fake fiancé? The whole idea was impossible.

"I'd better clean up the mess I made." Elissa began
gingerly picking up broken shards of the teacup. "Then
we'll have to warn Helen and Damien and get our story
straight. We don't have long."

Lucy's ability to speak clicked on and she jumped up.
"We?" She glared at Elissa and then at Jack. "We? I
hope you don't think I'll agree to this. First of all, there
aren't that many men hanging around that I can ask to
go along with such a crazy scheme. And secondly, I
can't lie. I've never been able to lie. It's hopeless." She

headed for the parlor exit. "I'm going to pack. Elissa, call the Springfield bus station and get me a ticket on the first bus to Kansas City. I'll hide out in the YWCA until he's gone. The Smiths are leaving for Springfield in the morning. I can hitch a ride with them."

She felt a hand take her wrist. "I'll do it, Luce."

Caught in Jack's firm grasp, she spun toward him as Elissa scolded, "You certainly won't do any such thing, Jack. Nobody's giving her a ride anywhere."

"I didn't mean that." He faced Lucy, towering there, all muscle and firelight. His bedroom eyes at half-mast, his features were unsmiling. "I meant, I'll pretend to be your fiancé." His voice was smoky soft, his glance strangely beguiling. She blinked, feeling out of breath as she focused all her senses on what he was saying. "You've known me a long time, Luce. We already care about each other. It wouldn't be that hard to pretend you love me—would it?"

Elissa gasped. "Perfection! Absolute perfection." Since her hands were full of broken pieces of china, she nudged Lucy in the ribs with her elbow. "And Jack's a lot better looking than Stadler. Taller, richer, and he has a strong, square chin, not that excuse for a jaw of Stadler's."

Jack grinned wryly at the redhead. "Stop it before I blush."

Elissa laughed. "*Really*, Jack. This is better than my 'kick me' sign idea. It'll destroy Stadler right down to his scummy roots." Elissa stretched up to kiss his cheek. "I'd better go throw this china away before I slash an artery. You two start planning Stadler's downfall."

When Elissa was gone, Lucy could only gawk at the man before her. "I—I won't let you do this."

He squeezed her wrist, his fingers lingering a second before he let her go. "Hey, if it weren't for the influence of your family, I might have traveled a very different

road in life.'' He shrugged his hands into his trouser
pockets. ''Let me help, Luce. I want to.''

''But I'm not a vengeful person. I wouldn't be able
to carry it off. Besides—besides…'' Her lower lip began
to quiver in spite of her attempt to quell it. Suddenly
overwhelmed, she dropped to the sofa, covering her eyes
with her fists. ''Oh, Jack—I waited so long for Stadler.
You have no idea what it's like to wait and wait for
somebody you love—'' A sob cut off her words.

The sofa dipped as he sat down, drawing her against
him. His solicitude was so welcome that she could no
longer hold in her gnawing heartache. He held her pro-
tectively, allowing her to cry herself dry against his
chest. Somewhere in her anguish, as he stroked her back
to calm her, she thought she heard him murmur, ''Maybe
I can imagine, Luce. Maybe I can.…''

Lucy looked up from polishing their silver tea tray at
the kitchen table as Elissa swept into the kitchen through
the pantry. Bella and her assistant had been scraping
food from the breakfast dishes and filling the dishwasher. ''Bella,'' Elissa called, ''could you and Ramona
excuse us for a minute?''

The plump cook looked a little startled, but nodded.
''Sure, Miss Elissa. Ramona and I were just going into
town to do some shopping for supper anyway.'' She indicated the kitchen door with a nod of her gray curls,
and her gaunt, plain-faced assistant scurried out ahead
of her without a word. Seconds later, the door closed,
leaving the sisters alone.

The guests had already scattered for the day, heading
off for sight-seeing in Branson and Silver Dollar City.
But Lucy's mind was on anything but the bounty of
things to do in their unique community, with its many
theaters and gala shows, nestled in the unspoiled Ozark
Mountains of Missouri. Her mind was raging, *Why am*

I still here? Why hadn't she packed her bags and left for Springfield the first thing this morning with the departing Smiths? She couldn't possibly have decided to go along with the plan to pretend to be engaged to Jack—could she? She took an extra hard swipe at the silver tray, a family heirloom, and gritted her teeth. Why, oh why, couldn't she *act*! Leave! Why did she have to be such a wimp? Why was she even listening to Jack and Elissa?

"Well!" her big sister interrupted the mutinous train of thought with a loud sigh. "I don't know what's the matter with our baby sister and her husband."

Lucy looked up, a tremor of alarm slithering through her. "Is something wrong? Are they okay? Are the twins—"

"Hold it." Elissa put a reassuring hand on her sister's shoulder. "I'm sorry. They're fine. I meant, when I told them about our plan, Helen started laughing. When she couldn't stop, she got after me for making her stitches hurt. Then she told Damien, and I could hear him laughing in the background." Elissa shook her head. "They have a strange sense of humor, those two. Do you think they've been snorting laughing gas?"

Lucy could feel heat creep up her face. She knew what Helen and Damien were thinking—*the myth*! That was foolish, of course. She had no intention of getting involved with another man, not now, maybe never. And Jack was merely a friend offering his assistance because he owed John Crosby, and he cared enough about her to want to help her save face. There was nothing more to it than that.

Swallowing, she set down the tray and eyed her sister as directly as she could. "How could you have told them such a thing? I'm not sure I'll agree to do it. As a matter of fact, I still think packing and getting—"

"Lucille Violet Crosby, you will not disgrace yourself

by turning tail and running. Is that clear?'' Elissa took up the polishing cloth and furiously began to buff the intricate pattern that banded the square tray, apparently trying to channel her fit of temper. ''Jack is willing. He cares for you. He cares for us all. Now you stiffen your upper lip and get with the program. Stadler Tinsley needs to be taken down a peg for his egotistical scheme, and you're going to find the backbone to do it.'' She plunked the tray onto the table and eyed her younger sister for a few seconds before her expression relaxed. ''Besides, once old Stad's hit in the face with the fact that you don't care about him, I bet he drags that un-fortunate new fiancée of his onto the first plane out of Missouri.'' Elissa brushed a hand through Lucy's white blond, shoulder-length hair, more as a sisterly caress than a gesture of grooming, though the stuff was so fine and flyaway it always needed a good finger combing. ''You'll have to pretend to be engaged for five minutes, tops.''

''You think so?'' Lucy wondered how it was that Elissa managed to make ideas that were completely in-sane seem perfectly reasonable. Probably some class she'd taken in law school.

''I know so.'' Elissa grinned, putting her arm around her sister and gathering her close for a peck on the cheek. ''Now that that's settled, I have an inn to run.''

As the redhead set off for the hallway, Lucy had a horrible thought. ''What about the help, Elissa? Bella, her assistant, Ramona, and the housekeeper, Jule?''

Elissa's features grew momentarily pinched, then she shrugged and grinned. ''Okay, so for five minutes they'll think you're engaged, too. No big deal.''

Elissa was gone before Lucy could come up with the obvious arguments. Like, what if Stadler saw through the lie? What if he stayed longer than five minutes? What if—what if…? She couldn't think of the other things. And even if she could have thought of any, she didn't want to dwell on them.

Shaking her head, Lucy slowly stood. *Pack*. That's what she had to do. She could always catch a ride to Springfield in Branson on one of the big hotel shuttles. There was no way she could carry off this charade even if Jack was willing to help. She wouldn't put him through it. It was too much to ask, even of him.

She must leave. *Now*.

Lucy checked her watch. Ten o'clock. Her cab should be arriving any minute. Snapping shut her suitcase, she headed out of her basement bedroom and hurried up the steps as quickly as her heavy bag would allow. She knew that Elissa would be in her office at this hour working on the inn's books, and Jack... Well, hopefully he was in his room or taking a nature walk in the woods—anywhere but in her direct escape route. She didn't want either of them to see her and try to persuade her to go through with their insane plan. At the top of the stairs, she hastened right into the little hallway that led to the staircase vestibule, then to the reception hall.

She could hear the crunch of tires on gravel as she reached the front door. Perfect timing. Peering through the beveled glass, she recognized the vehicle as a cab.

Taking a long, relieved breath, she knew she was about to make a clean getaway. Let Stadler think she ran away. Let him believe she was too hurt to see him. She didn't dare look into his two-timing, plum-colored eyes, eyes that she feared could still make her melt. She didn't dare let him see her pain.

Besides, Elissa had too much family pride to admit Lucy had run off. She would deny the truth with all her strength and make up some plausible story. This was the best way. If she stayed, there was no way she could hide her anguish. Stadler was not a stupid man.

Just as she turned the door handle, she heard the slam of a car door, then another. Two slams? Two car doors? For one cabdriver? Alarm constricted her stomach, and she peeked through the glass again, only to gasp out loud.

Stadler!

He and—and his *woman* were here.

"Luce?" The query came from somewhere in the vicinity of the staircase. She spun around. "What is it?" Jack came down the remainder of the steps and made quick work of the distance between them. "What's wrong?"

She shook her head, pointing disjointedly over her shoulder. Words wouldn't form.

He leaned close, his night-woodsy scent clean and pleasantly familiar as he looked through the frosted and cut glass. "The bastard?"

Though she was unsettled by his word choice, she knew whom he was talking about and nodded.

When he stepped back and looked at her again, he noticed the suitcase beside her and frowned. His glance flicked back to hers as realization struck. His look of disappointment almost made her cry. "Luce, you weren't." The words of disbelief came out in a husky whisper.

She swallowed hard several times. "I—I can't go through with it, Jack."

The flare of his nostrils was his only comment as he grabbed her bag and sprinted with it to the staircase hall. Throwing open the storage door below the stairs, he shoved it inside.

Lucy started to object, but jumped when she heard heavy footfalls on the front porch. As though it were a pack of rabid wolves bent on gnawing through the door, she leaped away. Even in her stumbling retreat, she couldn't keep from staring in hypnotized fascination at the crystal knob, twinkling as it turned.

There was a click and a low-pitched creak when the door began to open. It happened in a crazy slow motion, seeming to take forever. But after an eternity of ponderously ticking seconds, there he was.

Stadler Tinsley—the man Lucy had *thought* she would spend her life with. The drama teacher at the University of Kansas, who got a lucky break, being chosen for the lead in an off-Broadway production of Shakespeare's *Hamlet*. Naturally, for an aspiring thespian, it had been an opportunity he couldn't resist, even though he and Lucy were to have been married in only two months.

So he'd asked her to wait for him—a wait that had become two long years while he toured Australia—and apparently romanced and *won* another woman along the way.

Lucy was unsettled to note that he was still as disarmingly attractive as she remembered. Tall, lithe, he stood there, impeccably dressed, somewhat on the dramatic side. Not a hair on his sandy blond head was out of place. His dazzling plum eyes were bright in contrast to his milky skin. And as usual, his prominent, aristocratic nose was lifted a bit high for him to claim a shred of humility.

Lucy knew the second Stadler recognized the woman he'd so recently and heartlessly dumped. His lips lifted in a jaunty smile, and her heart twisted. How dare he smile like that, without a hint of remorse?

He stepped inside the door and lifted his arms as though he expected her to run to him in a spasm of joy. "Lucy, my pet!" His fine bass voice echoed as though he were speaking to an enraptured audience. "What a pleasure it is to see you again!"

He took a step into the room, then stopped, his cultivated smile faltering. Lucy was confused for a second, until an arm came around her waist, gathering her against a sturdy torso. She could detect Jack's cologne as well as the light, underlying tang that was his alone, and she breathed deeply, hoping that filling her lungs with his essence would infuse her with at least a *little* courage.

It was too late to run.

"Our sentiments exactly, Stadler, old buddy." Jack extended a hand toward the gaping man who had gone still. "Really—a pleasure. Isn't that right—darling?"

Lucy felt wretched. The fraud had begun.

CHAPTER THREE

A SANDY eyebrow lifted, the only indication of Stadler's misgiving. Though his smile had wavered temporarily, it was radiant again. "Why, Lucy-pet? What does this mean?" His arms slowly began to lower to his sides, giving the impression of a deflating plastic doll.

A rustling came from outside the door. "Staddie?" Another rustle and a thump-thump. "*Staddie*? Can you open up a little wider?" After one more dubious glance at the entwined couple, Stadler swung the front door wide to allow a petite woman to struggle in, a big leather suitcase in each hand. "I told the cabbie we could get the cases, Staddie. Save a penny, save a…" She looked up, smiling brightly at the room in general. "Well, whatever. I can never remember those old sayings. Hi, everybody."

Lucy stared at the young woman who was barely five feet tall. Her dark hair sprouted up and out, away from her head in a punk-pixie style that somehow suited her. By her beaming smile, she clearly didn't know the minefield she was stepping into. Apparently, Stadler hadn't thought the poor thing needed any preparation for what could very well be awkward—if not violent. He obviously didn't make a practice of giving bad news face-to-face. *Not a particularly heroic trait*, Lucy mused.

"Hi, there." It was Jack who broke the silence. With gentle fingers at Lucy's back, he prodded her reluctant body forward as he stretched out a welcoming hand. "I'm Jack Gallagher and this is my fiancée, Lucy Crosby. Nice to have you visit us, Miss…"

The pixie woman with huge hazel eyes let go of one

of the bags. Instead of extending her hand, she began to
rub her palm on the thigh of her mutilated jeans, seemingly cleansing it before the handshake. Lucy's glance
was drawn to her red T-shirt, taut over pert, unfettered
breasts that jiggled as she moved. The shirt read, "I am
woman, hear me charge."

After a thorough polishing of her palm, which now
had to be raw if not entirely germless, the pixie extended
her hand. "Sareena Green. Pleased to meet you, Jack—
Lucy."

"*Fiancée*?"

Three heads turned toward Stadler, who had now
lifted both eyebrows in conspicuous incredulity. His
smile was gone. "Fiancée?" he repeated, this time in a
deeper timbre, intimidating enough to make Lucy quake.

If not for Jack's arm around her, and his body to lean
against, she would have sunk to her knees. She swallowed hard, but found that all she could muster in answer was a panicked widening of her eyes.

"Exactly when did this happen?" He slanted his head
toward Lucy, one eyebrow cranked upward as though he
were saying, "Not a funny joke!"

"It was sudden," Jack offered, squeezing her waist
reassuringly. By his voice, she could tell he was smiling
and she turned to gape at him. His expression was amazingly believable. "I came for a visit and—well, the next
thing Lucy knew, she was engaged." He gazed down at
her, his smile tender. "Isn't that right, sweetheart?"

She nodded numbly. She had to give Jack credit. That
little speech was about as close to the truth as this
ghastly fiasco was ever going to get.

Startling her, he lowered his mouth to her temple. His
lips against her skin were warm and pleasant. His mouth
moved to caress her at her hairline as he added, "I don't
regret what I did, Tinsley." Lifting his lips away, he
faced Stadler. "I've loved her for a long time. This was

all my doing, so you mustn't blame Lucy.'' His jaw clenched, then clenched again as though he were making a guilty admission. ''I felt like a jerk—until your letter came.'' He grinned. But the expression wasn't particularly friendly. More cunning. ''But then, you know something about jerks, don't you, old buddy.'' It hadn't been a question.

Stadler's eyebrows snapped down in a grimace, and he peered sideways at Sareena. The poor thing's features were pinched in confusion. ''Ena, my pet, why don't we get settled? You look wan.'' He turned back to Lucy and managed a real smile. ''May we have a key? Perhaps we can chat about this later.''

Lucy felt a rock form in her stomach, so hard and painful she wanted to cry. *Later*? That one word held a horrid reality—Stadler had no intention of staying only five minutes. As she nodded, moving in a daze behind the reception desk to get him a key, she felt a sudden urge to feed Elissa piece by piece to the neighborhood squirrels. Five minutes, she'd said. She'd practically promised! *Why, oh why, am I not safely on my way to Kansas City right now?*

With a frail excuse for a smile, she handed Stadler a room key. Her fingers shook so badly the metal latchkey clattered against its plastic holder, sounding like a tambourine solo. When he reached out to take it, he startled her by engulfing her whole hand in his. ''What is it, pet? You seem agitated.''

She stilled, feeling caught. She couldn't lie! Didn't know how. She had told Jack and Elissa she couldn't carry this off. What was she going to do? *Blurt out the truth*! That seemed like the only answer. As the ugly facts scrambled to the tip of her tongue, she cast a helpless gaze toward Jack.

Almost as though he could read her mind, Jack moved forward, instinctively protective. With a casual maneuvering of his hand, he separated Lucy from her ex-fiancé and gave Stadler the key, all the while smiling easily. "You know our Lucy," he said. "She hates to hurt anyone's feelings, and she's upset about having to spring our engagement on you like this." He enclosed her limp hand in his so that her fingers were exposed. Rubbing them against his jaw in a loving gesture, he continued to smile at Stadler. "I told her that you—of all people— would understand how these things happen. You do understand, don't you?"

Stadler inhaled, lifting his regal, if slightly inadequate, chin. His narrowed glance shifted to Lucy. However, when he opened his mouth to speak, Sareena touched his sleeve. "What's going on? Why would you care if they got engaged?"

Stadler shot a look at his fiancée, his expression troubled for an instant before he could adjust his face in a tolerant smile. He tweaked her pointed chin. "Ena-pet, you look tired. Perhaps we should rest before luncheon." He lifted his scrutinizing gaze to Lucy. "We'll see you later, then?"

She nodded, apparently the only thing she was capable of doing in Stadler's self-assured presence. She couldn't recall opening her mouth once since he'd arrived.

Skimming Sareena with an offhand glance, Stadler indicated the stairs. "Come, Ena-pet."

He headed for the staircase, but was halted by Jack's hand on his shoulder. "This is a do-it-yourself place. Luggage won't get up there by itself. Or did you expect the lady to carry all the bags?"

Though Stadler was six feet tall, he was shorter than Jack by three inches. He gave Jack a fleeting glower, then backtracked to retrieve one of the bags. "I apologize, Ena-pet. I'm afraid I'm tired, too. I've forgotten my manners."

Sareena seemed startled, as though she carried bags

quite a bit without help. "Uh—thanks, honeybun. My guitar case is on the porch."

Looking put out, Stadler went outside and grabbed the instrument, then stalked past Jack without glancing his way.

Once the two newest guests had disappeared upstairs, Lucy planted her hands on the reception desk, half-sprawling across it, weak and sick to her stomach. She dragged her gaze to Jack's. "I can't do this."

He seemed to contemplate her for a moment, his features thoughtful. Finally, he lounged against the opposite side of the desk, placing a hand over hers. "You can, Luce. It's important."

She closed her eyes, gaining strength from his touch. Inhaling raggedly, she faced the fact that she had to follow through now that the lie had begun. Besides, Stadler deserved a little ego bruising—the mewling, letter-writing *cheat*! Slipping her hand from beneath Jack's, she rubbed her eyes, feeling caught between a rock and a hard place. "Okay..." She nodded, letting out a re-signed sigh. "What's next?"

"We play it by ear. Just follow my lead." His comment was soft-spoken and solemn, drawing her trusting glance.

The strange glimmer she saw in his slumberous eyes had to be a trick of the lighting.

"The twins look wonderful!" Lucy entered Helen's hospital room and hurried over to the bed, hugging her younger sister. "What are you going to name them?" Before Helen could speak, Lucy reached across her and squeezed Damien's hand. "Hi, Daddy. How are you feeling?"

He grinned. "My stitches are killing me and I hate the food, but otherwise I'm good."

Helen laughed, then winced at the discomfort it

caused. "Actually, the food's very tasty. And to answer your first question, we have no idea about names yet. What do you think of Gladiola and Goldenrod?"

Lucy stiffened, staring, not knowing what to say about the dreadful names. Damien's rich laugh made her realize Helen was joking. "Oh, thank heaven. I know we all have flowers for our middle names, but—there *is* a limit!" She sank into a nearby chair. "Really, what are you naming them?"

"We don't know yet," Damien said, standing. "I'm afraid we need help. I favor political names like Kennedy and Reagan, and Helen likes movie titles like Sabrina and Twister."

Elissa breezed in with Jack on her arm. "Okay, what did I miss?"

Joining in the fun, Lucy kidded, "We were discussing names for the girls. I think Twister and Hurricane might be nice. They're unique without being too outrageous. Right, Jack?"

He grinned at her, flashing straight white teeth. "What would you consider outrageous, Luce? Calling them after microbes with megasyllable names—say, for instance, Plasmodiophora brassicae?"

"Why, Jack," she teased, "that's really unique." Placing a hand to her cheek, she pretended to fall into deep thought. "Now what can we call the other one? Everybody think. What rhymes with—Plasmodio what's-it?"

"Jack, you made that up," Elissa said with a laugh.

He looked her way. "No, I didn't. It's a cabbage fungus." When his attention returned to Lucy, his smile was playful and elegant at the same time. "You'd be surprised what you can learn in the restaurant business."

Lucy's cheeks heated, and she had no idea why. "I'm impressed."

"Me, too," Helen chimed in.

Their shared laughter was a pleasant sound generated by a close family. Lucy relished this time of being together. Such moments came so rarely since Helen had married and moved away. And Jack was gone for years at a time. Lucy cherished the experience.

"Well, you all keep right on thinking," Helen said. "There's a *slight* chance something better might come along."

"I'm hurt," Jack kidded.

"You should be, wanting to name my beautiful girls after a cabbage fungus." Helen motioned him over to the bed. "But I forgive you. Now where's my kiss?"

He cast a roguish glance toward her hovering husband. "Does he bite?"

Damien took a seat in a chair beside his wife's bed, enfolding her hand in his. "How can I refuse a kiss to the first man my wife ever slept with?"

Jack's expression grew charmingly shocked. Helen reached out to him, urging him forward. "Damien heard how you let Lucy and me climb into your bed during thunderstorms. Remember?"

"Fondly." His smile reappearing, Jack gave Helen a kiss on her forehead. "You're a beautiful mother. But I always knew you would be."

"Damned beautiful." Damien shifted in his chair to kiss Helen's cheek. He whispered something in her ear, and Helen nodded as though urging him to say something. When he sat back, he scanned his blond sister-in-law with a grin. "So, Lucy, how's the engagement going?"

Lucy felt herself blush and grew tongue-tied.

"Great so far," Elissa said. "Lunch was interesting. Lucy even managed to talk a little. And she gazed into Jack's eyes once without turning a neon pink. I'm sure she'll get better with a little practice." The redhead took Jack's hand. "But our boy here is the natural actor. I'd swear he's really in love with Lucy.'' She nuzzled his knuckles against her jaw. ''I always knew your bad-boy past would come in handy for us Crosby girls.''

He smiled, and Lucy noticed a vague ruddy tinge to his cheeks. *Jack was embarrassed*. Her heart went out to him. ''Jack's a good friend,'' she said. ''Don't tease him, Elissa. You're such a troublemaker.''

The redhead spread her hands in a helpless gesture. ''Hey, if you'll remember, this engagement story was Jack's idea.''

''And how's Stadler reacting to the news?'' Damien asked.

Elissa shook her head. ''Who, Mr. Denial?'' She paused, looking reflective. ''You never met him, did you, Damien?''

''I never had the pleasure.''

''What pleasure?'' Helen mumbled, then clamped her hand over her mouth. ''I'm sorry,'' she said. ''That just slipped out.''

Lucy felt a twinge at her words and automatically defended him. ''Stadler can be enchanting and dear.'' She gave her baby sister a dark look.

''I said I was sorry.'' Helen looked contrite.

Elissa walked behind her sister's chair and began to rub her shoulders. ''You have to stop defending the guy, Lucy. He's not worth it. Just remember we love you and we want you to be happy.''

''I hope Stadler and his new fiancée don't leave before they can see our gorgeous baby girls,'' Helen said.

''*Bite your tongue!*'' Lucy cried. In the ensuing silence, she realized how rude she'd sounded. She shook her head, aghast at her uncharacteristic show of temper. ''I—I don't know how long I can carry off this lie. The sooner Stadler leaves the better.''

''Your muscles are all knots, honey.'' Elissa rubbed and massaged, glancing at Jack. ''Do you think—

maybe—this trick we decided to play on Stadler is too much for Lucy?''

"You finally figured that out?" Lucy admonished, jumping up. "*Fine timing*! Now that it's too late!"

The redhead looked stricken at her sister's rare explosion of fury. Her lips moved, but no sound came, and her green eyes began to glisten. It was clear from her expression that she finally understood what an ordeal this was for Lucy. Tears shimmered on Elissa's lower lashes. "Oh—oh, honey, please forgive me. I sometimes forget…" She stopped and swallowed as though trying to steady her voice. "I didn't understand…"

When Lucy saw how badly her sister felt, she began to hurt right along with her. She knew Elissa well enough to understand that she rarely cried, so her turmoil was deep and real. Unable to stay angry in the face of Elissa's distress, she rounded the chair and hugged her. "It's okay, Liss," she murmured brokenly. "He'll leave—soon. I can manage."

Elissa hugged her back, wiping her eyes with the heel of her hand.

Damien cleared his throat, sounding uneasy. "So, Jack, how long are you going to be in Branson?"

Lucy was grateful for the subject change.

"I'm not sure," Jack said. "I have a real-estate man looking at properties for me. I'm thinking of opening a Gallagher's Bistro here."

Lucy sniffed and turned at the news. "Oh, I'd almost forgotten." She brightened at the reminder. With an arm around Elissa's waist, she grinned at him. "Maybe you'll get back more often with a restaurant here."

He winked at her. "Absolutely."

"Well, Jack, have you two kissed yet?"

Jack's smile dimmed, and he stared at Helen, who'd asked the odd question. "Have I kissed the real-estate man?"

She giggled. "No, silly. *Lucy*. Have you kissed Lucy yet?"

His drowsy-lidded gaze widened a bit.

"For Stadler's benefit, I mean."

With her explanation, he nodded in understanding, then gave Lucy a quick, appraising look. "No—it hasn't been necessary."

"Necessary?" Damien asked. "When do engaged people need a reason to kiss?"

Lucy was flaming, her skin all but smoking. She knew what Damien and Helen were doing. The scheming rats! Well, she was having no part of it. Slipping her arm from around Elissa, she eyed Helen and Damien with as much indignation as she could muster. "Engaged people need a reason to kiss when they're not *really* engaged. That's when."

"Maybe they're right, Lucy," Elissa said, regaining her smile and sniffling into a handkerchief. "It might be smart for you and Jack to have a practice kiss." She stuffed the hankie back into her pocket. "So it'll look real."

Lucy glanced at Jack, who was watching her. She couldn't tell if his expression was disquiet at his distaste for the idea or if he was feeling sorry for her, knowing she was unhappy about it. Whichever, he looked far from delighted.

"Practice makes perfect," Helen said cheerfully. "And we're as happy as pie to help. Aren't we, Damien?"

"I know I'm happy," he drawled with a grin.

"You're all as nutty as pecan pie." Lucy's voice was low and uneven.

"Oh, Lucy, it's *Jack*, remember," Elissa chided. "You've kissed Jack before. A thousand times."

Shocked, she swung to stare at her elder sister. "But not—not on the lips! Not like a—a lover!"

Elissa shrugged. "Details."

"*Minor* details," Helen echoed.

"Kiss her, Jack. We'll score you." Damien casually entwined his fingers behind his head and lounged back in his chair. "Like in the Olympics." Lucy telegraphed her brother-in-law a sharp-eyed warning. He grimaced, letting her know he'd received her message, but all too soon his grin reappeared. "I'll be France, so if there's any French kissing—"

"Oh, *please*!" Lucy cut in, suddenly light-headed. She swallowed, going hot all over. Apparently, her blush had now traveled the length and breadth of her body. And there was something wrong with her heart rate. It had gone all erratic. She slowly faced Jack, disbelieving. "You—you don't agree with this plan? You don't think we should actually *kiss*?"

He grinned at her, and she relaxed, positive he was about to agree with her. "You don't have to say it like it's a prison sentence, Luce." She frowned, confused. That didn't sound as though he was agreeing with her. His perusal was steady. When he shrugged, her hopes were dashed. "It might not be a bad idea," he added softly. "If a kiss does become necessary and you stiffen up, then Stadler will know we're faking. And he'll have won."

"Besides, it might be—educational," Helen offered.

"Education is a wonderful thing," Damien said, and Lucy passed them both a hot glare that should have turned them to ashes—if the world were at all fair.

"Well, if it'll keep you from turning that neon maroon color and stiffening up like a stuffed flounder in front of Stadler, then it's worth a practice run," Elissa said, unaware of the unspoken battle going on between Lucy and the Lords. It was obvious that Elissa hadn't put any stock in the D'Amour myth and had forgotten about it. She flicked her wrist up to look at her watch. "Kiss her,

Jack. I have to get back to the inn. I'm interviewing for a new maid to help Jule out.''

Against her will, Lucy's glance was drawn back to Jack. He lifted a brow in a resigned gesture that was blatantly teasing. ''Elissa has to get back.''

She eyed the ceiling. ''This is silly. We won't have to kiss.''

''I bet that's why Stadler's still here.'' Elissa snapped her fingers, looking as though she'd had a revelation. ''That's got to be it. He hasn't seen any physical displays of affection between you two and he's suspicious. The man's shrewd, you have to say that for him.''

Lucy exhaled, suddenly freezing cold. It was weird how the air-conditioning in this place was so untrustworthy. One second she was boiling and the next she was shivering. The anxiety of having Stadler visiting, looking at her with those skeptical eyes, was playing havoc with her metabolism, weakening her resistance. If she hung around in the hospital much longer, she'd probably come down with something—pneumonia or hives or—or— that cabbage fungus.... ''Okay, okay.'' She gave up, shaking her head in surrender. ''Let's get it over with.''

Jack chuckled. ''Now there's a turn-on.''

She eyed him narrowly. ''Don't kid. I'm not in a very good mood.''

He made an apologetic face. ''Sorry.'' Stepping closer, he placed his hands on her shoulders and leaned toward her, then stopped, sensing resistance in her rigid stance. ''Ready?''

''You're not going to kiss her like that, are you?'' Dismay rang in Helen's voice. ''You could stick a grand piano between you two. Take her in your arms, Jack.''

Lucy twisted to eye her sister. ''Do you *mind*?''

Helen shrugged indifferently. ''Are you going to play a piano duet, or kiss? That's all I want to know.''

''I'm afraid I can't play the piano.'' Jack's joking admission ruffled Lucy's hair, drawing her gaze. He grinned his encouragement as his arms slid around her, tugging her into his hard, lean body. The feel of him was a shock—*a pleasant one*, some small part of her brain conceded—but a shock nevertheless. Unable to help herself, she went as stiff as wood. "Lucy..." he urged, his mouth brushing against her temple. "Don't fight me. This won't hurt."

She heard a sound, an odd, high-pitched gurgling, and realized it was coming from her own throat. *A giggle?* She was mortified. She certainly didn't feel like laughing, so where had that come from?

Now it was Jack's turn to stiffen. He pulled away. "Something funny?"

She shook her head, embarrassed to hear the hysterical tittering fill the air again.

"Are you tickling her, Jack?" Helen asked, sounding confused.

He frowned down at Lucy, his eyes flickering with frustration. "Luce, if you can't do this..."

"I can..." She giggled, then clamped her mouth shut to stanch the flow of inappropriate laughter. "I'm sorry," she whispered, sucking her lips between her teeth.

The very idea of kissing a man, even Jack, in front of so many gawking people was taking a toll on her tattered emotions. Laughter rumbled in her chest and she cleared her throat to quell it.

"Oh, fine," Jack grumbled.

She shook her head as if to say she was gathering herself and would be ready in a second. She cleared her throat and forced herself to mold her body into his. A new hysterical giggle threatened, and she choked on it.

He smelled nice—like Jack—and somehow that helped. Her limbs responded, calmed, her body easing further into his. With a quick breath, she snaked her arms around his waist. How trim and solid he felt under her hands.

"That's better." His face tilted down, his lips shifting closer to hers. "Lift your chin a little." Squeezing her eyes shut, she angled her face upward. She expected him to kiss her and braced for it. But nothing happened. She opened her eyes and found herself staring up into a narrowed, cinnamon gaze. "Lucy, I'll need your lips for this."

She frowned in mystification, then with a start realized her lips were still firmly planted between her teeth. She groaned. "Sorry…"

"Good grief, Lucy, get hold of yourself," Elissa said. "It's a kiss, not oral surgery."

Burning with humiliation, Lucy met Jack's gaze again. Something about the way his eyes were flashing made him seem the tiniest bit angry. She didn't have time to wonder at the cause, for at that instant his mouth covered hers, taking bold possession, his hands locking against her spine and crushing her into his hardness.

She'd expected his kiss to be soft, gentle—brotherly—but she'd been wrong. His mouth moving against hers was all-consuming—a sizzling, wordless seduction that seemed to say, *"Open your lips to me, Lucy. Let me explore, tempt, drive you wild."*

The scandalous message was so loud, so clear, she felt a lurch in her breast. Her eyes popped wide. Her arms became ramrods against his chest, and she pushed frantically, stumbling backward. "What was *that*?" she demanded breathlessly.

He straightened, his brow furrowed. "If you don't know, then I wasn't doing it right." His remark held a suggestion of huskiness. "Was it that bad?"

It wasn't bad! her mind screamed. *It was far from bad! It was—it was…* "It was bad! Very bad!" she lied, a quiver in her voice. "Let's not do that again, Jack."

Whirling to Helen and Damien, she sputtered, "And—and forget—forget *everything*, okay? Never bring it up! I'm not in the market for—for Olympic kissing or anything else!"

She stormed out of the room, upset, disconcerted. That had been a very bad experiment. How dare she feel *anything* in Jack's kiss? He was like family.

It was tension. That's all. She was stressed out. Not herself. Jack was doing her a favor. Just because he kissed like—like—well, like an Olympic kisser, that didn't enter into it.

Once outside, she sagged against Jack's car, then jumped away as though the touch was somehow illicit. She ran a hand through her hair, exhaling long and low. How foolish! It was Jack's rental car, for heaven's sake, not his lips.

She sucked in a breath at the sudden rush of memory. *His lips.* They were awfully sexy as lips went. She'd never thought of his lips in quite that way before—as a mechanism for kissing. No wonder teenage girls had climbed into his bedroom window all those years ago. She didn't blame them, the poor, helpless things. She shook herself mentally. She wouldn't think about it. She would put that bit of intimate knowledge about Jack on a back shelf in her mind and forget it.

Sagging against the car again, she prayed that Stadler and his pixie woman would flit out of town tomorrow morning. They *had* to, because there would be no more mouth-to-mouth kissing going on between Jack and her.

Absolutely none!

CHAPTER FOUR

LUCY felt like a jerk. How could she have treated Jack so shabbily, pushing him and going all hysterical? Even feeling as conflicted as she did, the ride home from the hospital had been unexpectedly light and lively, thanks to Elissa. Lucy blessed her older sister for keeping up an amusing dialogue about some of the most outrageous guests they'd had at the inn. If it hadn't been for the vivacious redhead, she was sure the ride back would have been a silent nightmare.

Lucy had purposely slipped into the back seat of Jack's rental car, seating herself behind her sister so that she could see his profile whenever she dared look his way. Though he laughed at Elissa's bubbly chatter, she could detect a certain rigidity of his shoulders, a tenseness in his jaw. It was obvious that she'd hurt his feelings with her childish display, and she despised herself for that.

He'd let them off at the inn and then driven directly into Branson, where he'd had an appointment with his real-estate man. He hadn't returned in time to eat dinner with them. Lucy had to admit that this latest meal under Stadler's scrutiny had gone more smoothly, since she hadn't been compelled to look lovingly at Jack, feeling like an impostor. Maybe it was a good thing that Jack was busy looking at properties in town, giving her a respite from his gaze, always fired with an unquenchable warmth. She needed time to get her wits together—and her apology to Jack worked out.

Now that dinner was over, most of the guests had left for Branson to take in one elaborate variety show or

54

another. All of the family but Lucy were gathered in the parlor—along with Stadler and his fiancée, of course. The last thing Lucy wanted to do was to be trapped in a room where he and his little twinkie waited like vultures. Well, not Sareena. She was as simple as a mouse, poor thing. But Stadler was waiting, no doubt with his forehead puckered, ready to pounce on any inconsistency in her ''engagement'' story. He no more believed that she was engaged to Jack than she believed it herself.

Well, she wouldn't go in there and allow herself to be interrogated. She would take a walk. Nippy weather or not, it was better than Stadler's artificially polite third degree.

Slipping on the overlarge sweater she'd knitted for her ex-fiancé as a welcome-home gift, she shoved up the sleeves, a new bout of irritation rushing through her. She would march through a tangled heap of cobras before she would give the handmade gift to Stadler now. Standing before the mirror, she decided the baby blue shade was fine for her light coloring and accented the blue of her eyes. And with today's oversize clothes, no one would know it had been meant for a man.

She had already changed into jeans and a soft white sweatshirt, so with the sweater she should be plenty warm if she walked briskly. She ran her fingers through her hair to move it off her face, only to have the fine tendrils tumble back to frame her bleak expression. She straightened her features. That guilty, unhappy look would surely give her away if Stadler saw it.

She tiptoed up the basement staircase, slipped out the kitchen door and bounded halfway down the stairs to the backyard before she realized someone was sitting on a step near the bottom. It wasn't hard to tell who by the width of the shoulders blocking her path. She grabbed the rail to keep from tumbling over him. ''Hi, Jack.'' Her voice was high-pitched with embarrassment. It was true that she planned to apologize to him, but it was also true that she wasn't quite prepared to do it yet.

He was sitting there, hunched slightly forward, his forearms on his knees, his hands clasped as though he was deep in thought. No longer dressed in a suit, he wore jeans and a dark mock turtleneck sweater that emphasized his upper torso.

He shifted to look her way. "Hi yourself." The light was quickly fading, but the flash of his teeth in a friendly grin was surprisingly calming. "Where are you running off to, Luce?"

She walked down the three remaining wooden steps to stand on the dry grass, then faced him. "I thought I'd take a walk rather than be stared at all evening by Stadler." She sighed and was startled by how forlorn she sounded.

Jack's expression grew serious and he patted the step he was sitting on. "Join me?"

She did want to be with him, actually, and that fact startled her. Nodding, she gathered the big sweater around her and sat down. There wasn't much room for them both, but Lucy decided that was good. Jack's warmth would help keep out the chill.

He glanced away from her as she settled herself, his attention drawn to the darkening forest behind the inn. The white picket fence that separated the yard from the woods looked ghostly pale by comparison. When Jack said nothing for a few minutes, she decided she had to start. "I—I'm sorry I was rude at the hospital."

He blinked and glanced at her, his face close, his gaze somehow sad. "You can't help how you feel, Luce." He turned away again. "It was my fault anyway. I shouldn't have kissed you like that."

Her cheeks grew warm even in the cooling night. "I—I'm…" She swallowed, not sure what she wanted to say, but knowing she had to say something to make things right between them. "It's just that I'm not all here emotionally—if you know what I mean—and I... When you kissed me like that—well, I wasn't prepared."

She stopped, swallowed, waiting for him to react. He did, but only with the clenching of his jaw.

She exhaled a quick breath, needing to get this over. "There's nothing wrong with the way you kiss." Her voice had gone peculiarly rough and she cleared her throat. "As a matter of fact, you kiss very well." She winced. That's not what she'd planned to say, and she wondered what idiotic part of her brain had insisted on the confession. She jumped when she sensed he was turning in her direction. She didn't know she'd unconsciously backed away from him until the square wooden rail support was biting into her shoulder.

With her retreat, he shifted so that he could lean against the wooden supports on his side of the steps. When he moved, their legs brushed. Lucy flinched away from the contact.

He watched her silently in the growing darkness for a moment, his expression thoughtful. "I'm sorry I frightened you, Luce." His voice was low, hardly more than a whisper. "I kissed you the way a man in love would kiss the woman he carried around in his heart. It was my mistake."

She shrugged dejectedly. "That's what you were *supposed* to do." She smiled, but it was more an ironic expression than one of pleasure. "I'm just too broken up inside right now to even playact with any conviction." She drew a breath in an effort to get through her apology. "It's not you or your kisses or your playacting that are at fault. You've been wonderful. It's me. *All me.* Don't let my emotional dilemma screw up your ego."

His eyebrows dipping, he took her left hand, startling her. "My ego's just fine, Luce. And you don't need to apologize for being honest. Let's forget it."

He shifted a hip and with his free hand drew something from his jeans pocket. "While I was in Branson this afternoon it occurred to me that you needed one of these." She felt warm metal being slipped on her ring finger and looked down. Something suspiciously like a diamond twinkled in the moonlight. "Engaged women get rings, I understand," he said. "We can tell Stadler it was being sized." He let go of her fingers, and when she looked up at his face, his eyes were on her, his expression unreadable.

She couldn't speak. Disbelieving, she dropped her gaze again to the sparkler on her left hand. It was *big*. Beautiful. She feared it might even be real. "Oh, Jack..." Wagging her fingers, the large, square stone caught the light and made it dance inside its many facets. "Oh, dear..." She gaped at him. "You didn't *buy* this, did you?"

He shrugged, crossing his arms before him. "Would you have preferred that I stole it?"

She tried to mouth several potential reasons why he shouldn't have done this, but no words formed. It was clear that she was allergic to diamonds—even fake ones—for her mind had turned to mush. Finally, at a complete loss, she stared down at the ring again—at the wide golden band adorned with the fabulous, glittery gem. "Please—please tell me this is a very good fake."

"Okay."

When he didn't go on, her glance shot to his face. Reading wry amusement in his features, she frowned. "Don't say things to appease me, Jack Gallagher. Is this ring synthetic or not?"

One eyebrow lifted in a vague shrug. "Not."

She groaned, sagging back. She'd been afraid of that. "What are you going to do with a diamond ring?"

He sat forward, resting one forearm on his knee. "Let's call it an investment."

Guilt strangled her so that she could hardly breathe, couldn't think. She tried to yank off the ring, but found it was too snug to be easily removed. She tugged harder, all too aware of Jack's history. She knew that his mother had married six times. Jack had told her he would *never* marry, not unless he felt in his heart that it would be only once—and forever. Jack Gallagher didn't take things like engagement rings lightly. "Jack, I simply won't let you do this," she cried. "Not to mention the fact that you must have spent a fortune on—"

"Well, there you two are!" Elissa called from the back door. "Stadler has been in a snit looking for you both." Lucy and Jack jerked around to see Elissa standing in the exit, clearly trying to bar the door to keep someone from muscling his way outside.

Just in time, Jack tugged Lucy against him, his arm slipping around her waist and drawing her close. His chin brushed the top of her head. "Hi, Elissa," he said, a smile in his voice. "I'm afraid we've been hiding out."

"I told everybody you two were—*oof*!"

Elissa stumbled sideways as Stadler forced his way onto the small porch, all smiles. "I was just telling your elder sister, Lucy-pet, that I was hoping we could get up a bridge game. Then I remembered how you loved to play."

Though nervous about this latest deceit, Lucy allowed herself to settle against Jack's chest. She even managed to smile at Elissa and Stadler, who shared the stoop above them, eyeing each other like gun-toting Hatfields and McCoys, bent on murder.

"Lucy doesn't like to play bridge," Jack said.

Lucy nodded in agreement, having forgotten how well Jack knew her. "Stadler, you're the one who loves bridge," she said. "I only played because you insisted it would be good for me—socially—to learn."

''And as you can see,'' Jack added, startling Lucy by kissing her temple, ''we're not feeling all that social right now.'' His hand around her waist was so toasty warm, so welcome, she found herself laying her hand atop his, lacing their fingers together. Apparently, the move caused her ring to sparkle in the light of the near full moon, because Stadler's gaze dropped and his mouth fell open.

''What's that on your hand?'' he demanded.

Lucy didn't say anything at first, thinking Jack would handle the lie. But when he didn't speak, she held up her hand so that he and Elissa could see the ring. ''What does it look like?'' She was amazed at the satisfaction in her voice.

Elissa gasped and raced down the stairs. She grabbed Lucy's fingertips. ''Oh, give me strength!'' She laughed. ''I hope *you* have the strength to lift that huge rock, sweetie!'' The redhead gave Jack a look. ''I *love* this, man.''

Lucy knew Elissa meant she thought getting the ring was about the greatest thing he could have done to insure that the ruse would work and that Stadler's ego would be cut off at the knees.

With a kiss first on Jack's cheek and then on Lucy's, Elissa turned to make quick work of the steps. Taking Stadler's arm, she said, ''Look, Stadler, can't you see they want to be *alone*? I swear, if a gorgeous man like Jack handed me a rock like that, I'd be giving him endless exhausting hours of thank-yous—if you get my drift. Let's go teach your little fiancée how to play cards. Did I ever tell you I'm a whiz at gin?'' She gave Jack a quick wink. ''That is, when *other* people don't cheat.''

The door slammed at their backs, and Lucy felt laughter gurgle up in her throat. This time, the sound wasn't a nervous twitter or a hysterical giggle, but real, merry laughter. She was surprised at the elation she felt. Maybe she did have a touch of vengeance in her soul after all. For the first time, she'd seen a glimmer of doubt in Stadler's eyes, possibly even pain, and she was stunned to find that it felt good.

"It's nice to hear you laugh, Luce," Jack murmured. "I want you to be happy."

She twisted around to face him, but didn't draw completely out of his grasp. With a kiss on his cheek, she smiled. "I'm so crazy about you, Jack. And don't worry about the ring. I'll give it right back as soon as Stadler leaves."

He smiled at her then, more an acknowledgment of her promise than an expression of relief. "I trust you'll do the right thing."

She had an overpowering urge to hug him and didn't fight it. She grasped him tightly around the chest, placing her face against his throat, relishing his nearness, his unwavering friendship—something she seemed to need more than food or shelter right now.

She was amused that he seemed startled by her impulsive embrace and she laughed again. For the first time since she'd received Stadler's cruel letter, she actually felt better. As his arms belatedly came around her, she whispered, "You're a great friend, Jack. I love you."

While he held her in his embrace, the strong beat of his heart was the only sound she heard, for he said nothing.

March twenty-second was a great day at the Crosby Inn. Helen came home from the hospital with the twins, and they all took up residence in Damien's room—the same room he'd been brought to unconscious and furious with the world when he'd first stayed there.

Who would have thought then that only nineteen months later he would return to the inn, a world-renowned author and political columnist, and that bashful but strong-willed Helen would be his wife and the mother of his two beautiful baby daughters. Lucy smiled at the thought. Life could certainly create enchanting love stories at times, and Lucy couldn't imagine two more deserving people.

That night, the belated birthday party was scheduled—now celebrating three birthdays instead of one. Lucy was elated to have her baby nieces share her special day. The only blot on the celebration was Stadler. *Why, oh why couldn't the sandy-haired fly in her personal ointment buzz off?*

By eight o'clock all the tourists had gone into town, so it was just the family to celebrate. Naturally, there was also the plump cook, Bella, and the housekeeper, Jule, and her husband, Hirk Boggs, the local butter-and-egg man. Since the Crosby sisters felt they were personally responsible for Jule and Hirk finding each other, the couple had become like extended family.

Lucy blew out the twenty-six candles on the huge sheet cake, then helped Helen and Damien blow out the single candles on each of the babies' cupcakes. "I hope they made a wish," Lucy said.

"Sure they did," Elissa said. "They wished somebody would come up with names for them so we don't have to call them Baby Doe One and Baby Doe Two."

She gave her brother-in-law a lawyerlike stare. "Just for the record, isn't it the law that you have to have the babies' names on their birth certificates *before* they can leave the hospital?"

Damien looked up at Elissa, a shock of dark hair falling over his eye patch. He grinned crookedly. "Not us. We're special."

"Come on," Elissa muttered, sounding frustrated. "Which one of these doll-babies is named after me? I'm sure one is, and I must start showering advice on her about how to become the first woman president of the United States.''

''We really haven't decided,'' Helen repeated, a twinkle in her eyes. ''Just be patient.''

''Lucy, help me here!'' Elissa cried. ''One of these darlings must be named after you, too. Aren't you crazy to know?'' When the redhead faced Lucy, she could see that her good humor was warring with her flash-fire temper.

Lucy pointed toward the cake, reminding Elissa of her job. ''The names won't matter. We'll all have starved to death. Now cut.'' She sidestepped away from the brush of Stadler's arm. She assumed it was accidental, but she didn't care to feel his touch or inhale his scent, constant reminders of their past.

In her escape, she stumbled into Jack and grabbed at his waist. He put an arm around her and gave her an ''are you okay?'' look. ''I didn't think you were the type to guzzle the cooking sherry,'' he kidded.

She righted herself, but left one arm circling his waist, finding the engagement charade somewhat easier today. ''Just tripped over Stadler's big feet,'' she whispered.

Jack glanced sideways to see Stadler very near, then whispered back, ''Care to go out on the front porch for some fresh air while they cut the cake?''

She decided it might be a good idea. Stadler's cologne was invading her senses and giving her a sinking feeling. His distinctive coconut-and-clove aroma always used to give her a thrill. Right now, her emotions were in such chaos she felt queásy.

She nudged Elissa. ''Call us when the cake is ready.''

Elissa glanced at her sister, appearing confused. ''Us?''

Lucy gave the redhead a ''don't be dense'' look. ''My *fiancé* and I are going for a stroll along the veranda.''

Elissa nodded sagely, her features easing. "Ah, good idea."

"Take your time, you two lovebirds," Helen chimed in. "Bella made enough cake for the entire state of Missouri. There'll be plenty left even if you don't come inside until Christmas."

The gathering tittered as Elissa went back to slicing the chocolate cake. Lucy cast one last glance at her baby nieces, sound asleep in their lacy white dresses, the black tufts of baby hair tied up with white ribbons. "Precious angels," she murmured, stopping by the double-size baby carriage to kiss each tiny pink forehead.

Before they could escape, however, Jule came rushing up, the brawny woman beaming, her brown eyes magnified behind thick, dark-framed glasses. "Happy birthday, Miss Lucy." She thrust out a thin, gift-wrapped package. "You don't think me and Hirk would forget your day."

As Lucy accepted the offering, gangly Hirk ambled up, carrying their four-month-old son, who was absolutely darling, with big brown, inquisitive eyes and lots of curly blond hair. Lucy decided Jule and Hirk had some surprisingly handsome genes in their combined pool and had a feeling their baby boy would be a striking young man one day.

As she opened the gift, she noticed that Jack continued to hold her around the waist. His touch held great comfort for her, and she found herself reveling in it. "Oh," she said when she opened the package. "Knitting needles. Just perfect for baby things." She looked up. "How kind."

Jule's wide smile revealed a missing incisor. "I didn't think you had that size needle." Her ruddy face grew ruddier, and she ran a callused hand through her cap of nutmeg hair. "Not since you made little Milhouse here that fine sweater and Hirk accidentally tossed that one knitting needle of yours into your growler.''

''Growler?'' asked Jack.

''Garbage disposal,'' Hirk supplied, grinning embarrassedly. ''I felt like a big old fool, I sure did,'' he said. ''Made a mess of your disposal, too.''

Lucy smiled and could feel Jack's chuckle where their bodies met. ''But, Hirk,'' she said, ''you paid for a new disposal. It wasn't necessary to—''

''We wanted to,'' Jule insisted, taking a fussy Milhouse from his daddy. ''Well, you two go on and take your walk.'' Her smile was so full of good wishes for the couple it made Lucy's buoyant mood sink. This falsehood of theirs was taking in way too many people.

''We'll see you later.'' Jack tugged her along, and Lucy had a feeling he sensed her quandary and wanted to get her away from the others before her face revealed the truth. ''That's a cute baby,'' Jack said, startling Lucy.

She looked at him with surprise. ''I didn't think men noticed such things.''

He glanced at her, one brow arching. ''What do you mean? I like kids.'' He turned away. ''I hope to have some of my own one day.''

She smiled at his handsome profile. ''I never thought of you as a father, Jack. You've always been so driven to succeed.''

He faced her again, and when he did she sensed several emotions flit across his face, but she couldn't quite pick them out before a casual smile settled on his features. ''Funny, I've thought of you as a mother.''

She laughed, shrugging. ''Well, I'm certainly not a career woman. And you can't make much of a living knitting sweaters. I suppose motherhood would come to mind.''

"I suppose." His chin came up in a half nod, his tone strangely flat.

"Too bad the name Milhouse is taken," she joked.

"Yeah, that's a real pity."

His chuckle was rich and intimate, causing an unexpected ripple of contentment to rush through her. She slipped an arm around his waist again, enjoying the easy camaraderie they shared. They turned a corner of the veranda that swept around the side of the Victorian inn, and she propped a hip on the porch railing, hugging herself.

Jack frowned at the move. "You're cold."

She had to admit it, and nodded. Though her sweater was somewhat warm for the parlor with all those bodies and the heat from the fireplace, it wasn't doing the job out here.

"I'll get your coat."

With her teeth threatening to chatter, she wasn't in the mood to argue. "In the basement apartment. The white wool jacket in my closet."

He grinned. "Right. Anything else? Yarn, maybe?" She was confused until he tugged the little gift box from her fist. "I thought you'd like to knit yourself a blanket."

She rubbed her hands together for friction warmth, smiling at his joke. "I'm fast, but not that f-fast."

His expression grew skeptical. "Are you sure you want to stay out here?"

"Completely." She had no intention of inhaling any more of that coconut-clove smell of Stadler's for a while. It unsettled her, and she wasn't sure if it was because she desired him or loathed him. With a playful shove at Jack's chest, she urged, "Now go. I'll be all right."

"I'll hurry." With that, he rounded the corner and was out of sight.

Lucy turned to admire the night. The sky was clear

and she could see the treetops wagging in the evening breeze, new leaves visible on tree branches only recently winter nude.

The waning moon was high and yellow. As an owl hoo-hooed somewhere in the distance, she inhaled the crisp, nutty scent of the Ozark Mountains. A shiver ran through her and she rubbed her arms, resting back against a wooden porch support.

Footsteps echoed nearby and she looked around with a smile, expecting to see Jack. Before she could speak, her smile faded and her heart lurched. Stadler was strolling toward her, intent sparking in his eyes. "I can't believe he left you out here in the cold." With a swift shrug, he removed his tweed sport coat and placed it around her shoulders, tugging the lapels together beneath her chin. As he did so, his knuckles brushed her throat. "Better?" he asked, his smile dazzling.

She had opened her mouth to deny his suggestion that she'd been left alone to freeze, but his beguiling eyes and heart-stopping smile shut off her ability to speak. There was that tiny dimple beside his mouth, the one that used to set her heart to fluttering. Moonlight enhanced it and did flattering things to his face. His plum eyes shone like pewter in this weak light, a sight to behold.

"'Journeys end in lovers meeting.'" He lifted her right hand and pressed a warm kiss on her knuckles. She shivered with the contact, her body fighting old needs, old longings. Then he deliberately lifted her left hand to inspect the ring, his glance narrowing. "I don't think you're as indifferent to me as you pretend, Lucy. When I touch you, you respond to me." He bent to kiss her, but she managed to jump from her perch, taking an evasive side step.

"I'm just cold, Stadler," she cried weakly. "Don't assume anything so crazy." It was hard getting words past the lump in her throat. She hated reacting to his nearness, but she couldn't help herself. Old habits of loving someone seemed to be hard to kill off, no matter how badly they might need killing.

He smiled again, revealing that same damnable dimple. His eyes glittered seductively as they searched her apprehensive face. "Then why are you afraid of my kiss?"

"I'm not afraid!" she retorted, wishing it was true. "It's—it's just that I'm *engaged*! And so are you! *To other people*!"

He drew nearer. Taking her shoulders, he pulled her close, grazing her forehead with his lips. Her nostrils filled with his smell. How many times had she dreamed of this moment—of being alone with him again in the moonlight? She winced at the reminder, her emotions in chaos, part of her brain screaming for her to run away, another part slyly cajoling her to lean into him, to make things go back to the way they were.

But she couldn't move either way. She was torn between right and wrong, fact and fiction. Which was which? What was right?

"I'd forgotten how beautiful you are," he murmured. "I know I hurt you, pet, and I'm devastated for that. Can you forgive me?" He kissed her forehead again, this time a little lower, nearer the temple. Lucy had a feeling he was working his way toward her mouth and she panicked. What would happen when he got there? Did she dare allow him to kiss her on the lips?

She didn't dare! She couldn't! "I—I forgive you, Stadler. If that's all, I think you should go." Her voice was hardly more than a squeak.

He smiled down at her, the allure in his eyes taking away her breath. This time, his kiss grazed her cheek. Her stomach tightened with indecision. Did she want him to kiss her or didn't she? "I think you still want me," he coaxed, "and I know I want you."

She gaped at him, speechless. What was he saying? Did he really want her back? Was he dumping the little mouse he'd dragged all the way to Missouri with him? Her brain was numb; she didn't know how to react. "What—what are you saying, Stadler?"

He caressed her hair, and against her will she leaned into his touch. "I'm saying I don't believe you sneaked around behind my back. It's not like you. I think Jack is merely being protective. I don't harbor any bad feelings toward either of you for your deception. I even understand why you did it. But I'm not a fool, Lucy."

"Stadler..." She lost her voice. She was terribly confused. He was so near, wanting her again. But he wasn't saying anything about breaking up with his current fiancée. She didn't know what she was going to do—what she should do—not even if he begged her to marry him this minute. But she knew she owed it to herself to hear it from his own lips before she could make any decisions. "What about your fiancée, Stadler?"

He cupped her face between his hands, bending closer toward his ultimate objective. "Sareena isn't a factor in this, Lucy. This is just between you and me."

She blinked, bewildered. What did he mean? Somehow, it sounded as though he planned to have them both. Sareena as his wife and Lucy as his—his...

The notion stumbled and skidded around in her brain for a few seconds before the truth finally hit, and hit hard. *Stadler was offering her a sleazy backstreet affair!*

Jack had told her Stadler's ego was raging out of control, but she'd had no idea he was so egomaniacal as this. Anger billowed inside her. How dare he make such a slimy proposition? And how dare he not believe that she could attract a good-looking, dynamic man like Jack? That last insight really pricked her pride. Just as his lips were about to touch hers, she put her hands on his chest, bent on pushing him away.

The sound of swiftly advancing footfalls caught her attention, and she turned in time to see Jack stalking around the corner, his expression hostile. It was all too clear by the fire in his eyes that he'd heard everything.

When he reached Lucy and saw her wearing Stadler's jacket, he slipped it off and thrust it into Stadler's gut. "Careful where you put your—*jacket*—or you'll be scratching around in the dirt for your pretty, capped teeth." He settled Lucy's coat around her, laying a sheltering arm on her shoulders before he confronted Stadler again.

The shorter man pulled up to his full height, looking like a belligerent bulldog. "Don't think you can intimidate me, *friend*. You're not engaged to Lucy and I know it. Do you think I'm a complete fool?"

Lucy was startled by Jack's sarcastic chuckle. "If you want my personal opinion, *friend*, you're the world's biggest fool." His voice had gone cold, and she could feel his rage pulsate through his body, experienced it in the tightening of his arm around her.

Somehow, his nearness made her mind clearer on what had just happened, and her animosity at what Stadler had suggested flared higher. There was something very reassuring about the fact that Jack's anger matched hers—maybe even exceeded it. Grateful for his loyalty, she lifted a hand to place it over his and squeezed his knuckles.

"For your information," Jack was saying, "Luce and I *are* getting married. Next week, as a matter of fact."

She sucked in a breath. Surely she'd heard him wrong.

"Married?" Stadler repeated, sounding thunderstruck. "Next week?"

An ominous silence fell over them like a shroud, and

Lucy felt faint. If Stadler had heard the exact same thing she had, then…

Stunned, she swung to look at Jack. His features were grim, his stare so threatening she was surprised that Stadler didn't turn tail and run. She'd hardly ever seen Jack angry, and the lightning-bolt flashes in his eyes, the jerking muscle in his cheek, were an awe-inspiring, intimidating sight.

Taking in every enraged signal he gave off, she scanned his features cautiously, trying to read his mind.

Marriage? Next week?

What in heaven's name did Jack think he was doing?

CHAPTER FIVE

Lucy was running on pure adrenaline as she dragged Jack down the stairs into her basement bedroom. With the slamming of the door, she whirled to face him, her emotions so jumbled she couldn't make them out. She was angry, yes. But at whom? Was she mad at Jack for making such a statement? *Marriage? Next week?*

Or was she angry at herself for nearly being drawn back into Stadler's spell, nearly allowing herself to be kissed? She didn't know, didn't dare analyze her feelings. She didn't want either to be true. She didn't want to be angry, had spent her life smoothing everybody else's feathers. So she just stood there, teeth clenched, glaring at Jack as he warily eyed her, waiting for the explosion.

"What are we going to do now?" she finally demanded.

His eyes narrowed at her angry tone, as though it pained him, but he didn't speak, merely continued to lounge against the closed door, looking at her.

His lack of response and her panicked need to have this whole thing go away became too much for her to hold inside any longer. She marched up to him and punched his stomach. The contact was surprisingly hard and her knuckles stung. He grunted and winced, spreading a hand over the spot below his rib cage where she'd bashed him.

"*Well*?" she ordered, near tears.

When she made a move to punch him again, he quickly closed his fingers over her fist and held tight. "Whoa, Luce." He looked serious. "I'm thinking."

Dismayed by his inadequate reply, she jerked her hand free and lifted it threateningly under his nose. "You're *thinking*? I should pop you again, Jack Gallagher! You certainly weren't thinking when *you* were making promises *we* can't keep!"

Even though his demeanor was serious, his lips twitched at her threat. "Pop me, then," he said. "I deserve it." He cocked his head, angling it for her to take a shot at his face. "I got mad and I said something I shouldn't have. So hit me." He pointed to his right eye. "Hard. Right there. Like when we were kids."

Startled by his offhand concession, she reared back with her fist, her anger blazing. But when actually faced with the reality of slugging Jack in the eye, she couldn't do it. She'd never hit anyone in her life before—well, except for Jack. She'd slugged him once. Blacked his eye. But she'd been a child then. She was a grown-up now and she wasn't a violent person. Besides, hitting a man who was aiming his eye right at you didn't seem very sporting. Frustration overwhelmed her and she spun away. Running to her bed, she spilled across it, unable to hold back a sob.

The mattress dipped when Jack sat down. She felt his hand on her hair, brushing it, smoothing it. "This was worse, huh?" he asked. "Worse than when we were kids and I dragged you off the ladder before you could rescue Helen's cat from the roof? You took a swing at me that almost knocked my lights out."

She gritted her teeth and wiped at her eyes. She remembered. Helen had been crying, hysterical that her cat was in danger. Elissa was having a yelling fit, telling Lucy she was going to get killed. And since the redhead wasn't much bigger than her sister, she couldn't forcibly keep Lucy from going up the ladder. So, instead, she ran to fetch Jack.

Lucy supposed he'd done the right thing—that time.

But that situation was totally different. Though she trembled with the urge to shout that at him, she didn't respond. Couldn't trust her voice.

"Lucky your dad got home then and rescued Pumpkin—and me." Jack stroked her hair. "I had to drag you out of there because I didn't want you to get hurt."

"Go away, Jack!"

"Don't you see, Luce? I had to do the same thing with Stadler." His hand stilled at her nape, lingered for a few seconds, then lifted away. "Admit it." His voice changed, hardened. "You were going to kiss that ass."

"I was not!" She rolled over to glare at him, swiping at her tears. He frowned at her, his eyes glimmering with a mixture of doubt and anger. For some reason, she couldn't meet that gaze and shifted to stare at the ceiling. "Well—I'm pretty sure I wouldn't have." She gulped, feeling a tiny bit guilty and not sure why. "Anyway, it's no big deal. What's one kiss?"

She heard him mutter an oath and couldn't help but look at him. He pushed a hand through his hair, mussing it. "It wouldn't have stopped at one kiss, Luce, and you know it. The man still has an effect on you."

Her cheeks heated. She supposed there was a grain of truth to his statement. "What if he does?" She glared her defiance. "What difference would it make?"

His eyebrows dipped and his lips opened slightly. He looked as though he'd been punched again, but this time by a more powerful fist than hers. "What difference?" His tone was incredulous. "Hell, Luce, do you have any idea what it's like to love someone when that person loves someone else? Trust me. It's not a good way to live. I don't want that for you."

Confused by the harsh emotion in his features and his voice, she pushed up on her elbows, glowering at him.

"Oh, Jack, what would you know about loving someone who didn't love you back?"

He had shifted his gaze away, but with her cynical question he pinned her with solemn eyes. "What would I know?" His lips curved in an ironic smile. "You don't believe in my thirty-three years I haven't run across somebody I can't have?"

"No." She sat up, sweeping her hair back. "I can't imagine it." She felt less angry now, more curious. She didn't think anybody on earth could find Jack wanting, once they got to know him. "Who is this demented woman who loves some other man more than you?" She scooted on the bed to lean against the wall. Clasping her hands in her lap, she was ready to listen. "Give me her number. I'll have a talk with her."

He smiled, though his eyes seemed sad. "Someday, maybe we can discuss it. But right now, we have a bigger problem."

She sucked in a hoarse breath at the reminder, and depression engulfed her again. "That's putting it mildly, Mr. Fix-it." She closed her eyes and lolled her head back in dejection. "If we don't get Stadler to leave before next Saturday, we may *have* to get married." She nudged him with her foot. "Maybe we should have a big fight and break up."

He put a hand on her tennis shoe, drawing her gaze. "He'd know it was a sham."

"So?" The word held a note of hysteria. "Maybe that's for the best."

He eyed her with intense frustration. "You really want to be that slimeball's mistress?" His tone was so fierce that a woman who didn't know him as well as she did might have cowered in fright. She felt pressure build on her shoe and pulled out of his grasp to indicate that he was hurting her.

They exchanged hard looks for a long time while

Lucy fought a battle in her head—a battle between right and wrong. Pro and con. Her emotions screamed, *This thing between Stadler and me isn't Jack's business! Maybe I want my ex-fiancé back on any terms*! Her intellect intruded, clamoring back, *How dare Jack even ask such a stupid question! The last thing on earth I want is to be any man's mistress*! A clear, vivid picture of sneaking around to meet Stadler in cheap motels filled her brain, disgusting her, making her sick to her stomach. That was no life. Jack was right about that.

Finally, her good sense won out and she slowly shook her head. ''No—no, I don't want that,'' she admitted. ''In my mind—when I let myself think about it rationally—I know he's a jerk and I don't want him back. But...''

Jack cleared his throat and moved across the bed to sit beside her, settling against the wall. ''Yeah, I know.''

She turned to look at him, then poked his arm with her elbow. ''Right. That stupid girl who doesn't love you.''

He shifted toward her, his mouth softening in the bare beginnings of a smile. ''You think she's stupid?''

Lucy shrugged. ''Has to be.''

He chuckled, but the sound lacked validity. Leaning his head against the wall, he stared straight ahead. ''What if we got married?''

She squinted at him. ''Who? You and Miss Stupid?''

''No.'' Reaching across her, he lifted her left hand so that she could see the twinkling engagement ring. ''You and I.''

Pulling from his touch, she drew up on her knees to stare, wide-eyed, at him. ''Have—have you lost your mind?''

The silence that followed buzzed in her ears like a persistent gnat, battering her already frayed nerves. Finally, he half smiled. ''I don't think that's one of the top ten answers a man hopes for when he proposes to a woman.''

She could only stare.

He shrugged at her lack of response. ''Okay, maybe I don't mean a real marriage. We can fake that, too. Have a little ceremony here in the inn. Get somebody to pretend to be a minister.''

She blinked. What language was he speaking? Nothing he was saying made sense. Feeling weak, she sank to the bed.

''Luce? Are you okay?''

She attempted a dry swallow, then shook her head. ''I—I thought you said we could fake a *marriage*.''

''Only if we can't get Stadler to leave first.''

So he really had suggested a fake marriage. She was too shocked to move for nearly a whole minute. She just gawked at him as he lounged there on her bed, a very large, very arresting presence in her small, drab room.

''Next Saturday night, then? You and me—holy wedlock?'' His grin was crooked, teasing.

Dread slithered across her flesh at the idea of going through with such a colossal lie. Her chagrin must have shown in her expression, for his smile died and he frowned. Leaning toward her, he took her hands, but she shied away.

''Damn,'' he muttered. ''Don't hate me, Luce.''

A strange fog seemed to have engulfed her brain. She didn't know what she felt. The world had become an unstable place she no longer recognized. The man she'd been engaged to for two years was suddenly engaged to someone else, yet he was here, propositioning her. And this man, Jack Gallagher, was a man she'd known and loved for over fifteen years—like family. But suddenly he was her fake fiancé, whose erotic kiss she was trying hard to forget and who had just announced their wedding

date. Next week. She didn't know what was real anymore, and what wasn't.

One thing she was sure of—deep down—and that was
that she felt no hatred in her heart for Jack. She hated
the lies and the pretenses, but not the man. Averting her
gaze, she shook her head, conceding through a sigh, ''I
could never hate you, Jack.''

''I'll hold you to that,'' he said softly.

With her head down, she gazed up at him through her
lashes. He was smiling at her, and even in her despair
her spirits lifted at the sight.

''Look at the bright side,'' he said. ''Maybe Stadler
will be abducted by aliens between now and Saturday.''

Lucy cast him a dark look. ''How can you joke?''

She started to get off the bed, but he took her wrist.
''Wait.''

She turned back, suspicious, almost fearful of what
was coming. She didn't know what to expect from Jack
anymore. He'd been behaving *differently* in the past few
days. Apprehensive, she didn't pull free, but went rigid,
instead. Though his hold on her wrist was gentle, he
effectively held her captive. What was he up to now?

He reached into his trouser pocket and drew out a
small box. ''I never gave you your birthday present.''

She eyed the package with distrust. ''I think you've
done way too much already.'' The statement came out
like an accusation.

A rueful smile edged his lips, then reached into his
eyes. ''Hell, it won't bite, Luce.''

When he let her go, she tentatively accepted the diminutive package, but didn't open it.

''Do you want the bomb squad to check it out first?''

She eyed him mistrustfully, then with an uneasy hitch
of breath began to untie the pink ribbon. Once she'd
removed the white paper, she lifted the lid to discover a
small, golden angel pin, the halo a semicircle of tiny

diamonds. Though she tried to hold on to her stern expression, she lost the battle when her gaze met his—warm and affectionate. His face grew blurry as her heart filled with gratitude. "An angel," she murmured, wiping away a tear with the back of her hand.

"It should be no surprise by now."

Her lips trembled into a smile. Jack had told her that the first time he saw her, when she was eight years old—with her light blond hair tumbling about her shoulders and dressed all in white—he'd thought of her as a little angel. So every year on her birthday, he'd given her some kind of angel—inexpensive trinkets, earrings, bargain-basement porcelain figurines.

When Jack was eighteen, his mother had run away with another man. Jack had been too ashamed to stay on with the Crosbys and had left with only his meager belongings. He'd gotten a job as a dishwasher in a local café, and since he'd had little money, he'd carved an angel for her eleventh birthday. Lucy never told him, but that was the angel she cherished the most. Lifting the golden pin from its box, she opened the clasp and fastened it to her blouse.

"Thank you, Jack." This time, she managed a genuine smile. "It's perfect."

His lips twisted wryly. "I know. I'm a prince."

She giggled, then sobered, shaking her head at him. "We're in such trouble. What is it about you, Jack? Why do I feel like punching you and hugging you at the same time?"

He leaned back against the wall, watching her. "You tell me."

She frowned at his slippery nonanswer. Even miffed at him, she moved to sit by his side. Settling back, she laced her fingers with his and squeezed. He squeezed back, and it felt nice.

This was good. This was companionable. *This* she understood. They were friends again. They would sit here like two old pals and think and think and think. Solve this thing once and for all.

A lot of absolute quiet took up the next fifteen minutes. Lucy hoped during all that silence that Jack was coming up with something brilliant because she was drawing a blank. At last, with a downhearted sigh, she asked, "What should we do, Jack?"

He shifted to meet her gaze. His lashes were long, yet all male. His gaze was intelligent and assessing—and stunning—as he scanned her face.

"What?" she asked, her pulse increasing. She told herself the feminine reaction was from anticipation about what he was going to suggest, *not* his nearness. "What have you thought of?"

"If we want Stadler to leave before Saturday…" He shifted nearer. Their bodies touched, hard communicating with soft, and she was startled by how aware she was of the minor contact. "I think," he went on, "we should start sleeping together."

Though Saturday was sunny and warmer, there was nothing but icy misery in Jack's soul. He flicked his wrist to look at his watch. Ten o'clock. He had an appointment with his real-estate man in an hour. It was still too early to leave the inn. Exhaling a curse, he tried to relax in the big wicker porch chair and stared heedlessly at the manicured front yard, carved out of the surrounding wood.

He heard a sound and turned in time to see Damien seat himself in the wicker chair beside his. It was all Jack could do to acknowledge the man. Dammit! He should have left the inn, just driven around. He wasn't in the mood for chitchat.

"So," Damien said, "I hear you're sleeping with Lucy."

Jack gritted his teeth. Not only wasn't he in the mood for chitchat, he didn't feel like playing the part of the lascivious interloper in a confrontation with the male head of the family. He had no intention of debating any alleged deflowering of the lovely Lucy.

Setting his elbows on the chair arms, Jack templed his fingers in front of his face and counted to ten. He liked Damien and didn't want to argue. As calmly as he could, he asked, "Where's Stadler?"

"In Branson." Damien crossed one leg over the other, his ankle on the opposite knee. "It seems that Sareena wants to be a singer. She wheedled at old Stad all during breakfast to take her to some shows." He chuckled wryly. "I think they'll be gone for a while. She's good."

Feeling thwarted, Jack closed his eyes. That meant they would be back. "Damn." He cast Damien a glance out of the corner of his eye. "Look. I'm not sleeping with Lucy, so you can lose the dueling pistols. I'm using the foldout sofa in the basement sitting room. We just thought Stadler would give up his game if he knew Lucy was…" He stopped, swallowed bile, unable to say it.

"I know," Damien said. "If she was sexually involved with somebody else."

Jack nodded wearily. Sinking back, he rested his head on the tall chair back. He needed to get as far away from this place as he could, as soon as he could. This whole engagement plan had been a mistake. "Why can't that ass just leave?" he muttered.

"Hey, man," Damien said after a moment. "How about a little advice? From one man crazy in love—to another."

Giving Damien an ominous look, Jack sat up. "What the hell are you talking about?"

Damien ran a hand through his black hair, but an unruly clump fell back across his eye patch. "I was a CNN reporter for a lot of years. I read people pretty well.'' He smiled companionably. ''I know you love Lucy.''

Jack's gut clinched. It was the truth, so why did hearing it aloud unsettle him? Maybe because even when he'd first seen her and had fallen in love, he'd known that he wasn't good enough for her. He was a dirt-poor kid with a tramp for a mother, a kid with one foot in juvenile detention.

He'd lived in a two-room walk-up where, if there wasn't a current ''daddy'', there had always been plenty of ''uncles'' hanging around. Oh, his mother was beautiful and had known how to work men.

She'd hit the jackpot on marriage number four, with upper-middle-class John Crosby. And for three years, Jack had had a real home, with clean sheets and three square meals a day. He'd had a stepfather who treated him like a flesh-and-blood son, and he had three stepsisters who adored him.

He hadn't been good enough for Lucy then, so he vowed that he'd make it in the world, and when he did, he'd come back for her. Only, when he was finally ready, she was engaged to someone else.

Then suddenly, miraculously, on his impulsive visit to Branson five days ago, his chance had been dropped into his lap—a chance to show Lucy his love, to make her see that he was the right man for her. But she couldn't see him that way. Didn't love him the way he loved her. Hell, he wanted to get as far away from her as he could. The pain of knowing he could never have the one woman he'd ever loved was too cruel. Only now, with this engagement story, he was stuck, at least until Stadler left.

Unable to completely deny a passion that he'd carried around for so many years, he said, ''I love all the Crosby girls.''

''I know you do.'' Damien leaned in Jack's direction.

''They love you, too. You're practically a saint in their eyes. You've always been there for them when they needed you. And that's great as far as it goes, but...'' He reached out and pressed Jack's shoulder in a friendly gesture. ''Do you know the old saying about how 'a man chases a woman until *she* catches him'?''

''Sure,'' Jack said, confused by the change of subject.

''Do you suppose it might work the other way around?''

''Work?''

Damien released Jack's shoulder and stood to face him. He held out a hand and opened it, palm up. ''Let's say this is Lucy's hand.'' He touched his palm. ''You're right in there, Jack. She has you.'' He dropped his arms to his side. ''How can the poor kid discover she *wants* you if she already has you?''

Jack looked at Damien, dubious. ''Why are you telling me this?''

Damien's grin was wry. ''Let's say I'm not above giving fate a nudge.''

Jack grunted caustically, casting his glance away. ''Fate's going to need one hell of a big nudge. Lucy doesn't see me as anything but a friend.''

''Trust me, Jack. You do your part, and Lucy will do hers. She won't be able to help herself.'' Mystified by the cryptic remark, Jack turned back, and Damien offered his hand. ''Okay?''

Jack accepted, but continued to frown. ''I don't know what we're shaking on, but—okay.''

Damien winked. ''Any man who's made a million bucks by the time he's thirty-three is bright enough to figure it out.''

When Damien reentered the inn, Jack sat back, puzzling over their conversation.

The next time he looked at his watch, thirty minutes

had passed. When he got up to head into town, he was smiling.

Lucy skipped down the basement steps two at a time. Playing with the twins gave her such a lift. She burst through the basement door and spun around the corner into the sitting room that had been her bedroom before Helen left and had recently become Jack's. It surprised her to see that he'd already folded out the sofa and was sitting in bed, covered from the waist down. Shirtless, he was going over a stack of printouts.

She scanned his upper torso, bronze and brawny in the lamplight. His chest was muscled, just silky enough with hair to make him quite a masculine picture. She felt an appreciative zing at the sight. "Aren't you cold?" She cleared her throat, wondering why her voice had gone shrill.

He looked up from his papers. "I'm hot-blooded." He grinned. "How were the twins?"

She laughed and came over to sit on the edge of the bed. "You mean Little Elissa One and Little Elissa Two? They're fine."

Jack laid aside his work. "So they're *both* named after Elissa now?"

"Well, Elissa said if Damien and Helen wouldn't tell her which one was *hers*, then she would claim them both." Lucy rested on one arm, grazing his leg with her hand. "Tonight Helen was calling them Sonny and Cher. Elissa was livid."

Jack laughed, and Lucy enjoyed watching his face. He had a great mouth, firm but kind. And his eyes. Compelling within the dark frame of his lashes. "I gather Stadler and Sareena have returned from their day in Branson?"

She sobered, nodding. "Yes. That's why I decided I'd

better come down here." She shrugged. "You know—
the sleeping-with-you thing."

His smile faded a little. "Right."

She glanced at the scattering of papers. "What are
you doing?"

"Going over the printouts of properties for sale here
in Branson."

"You want to play some cards when you're done?"

He grinned at her, then shook his head. "Won't have
time tonight. I need to get some work done. After I do
this, there's the usual restaurant business. You know
how it is."

She felt a rush of disappointment, but she understood.
"Sure."

He cupped her chin in his hand and eyed her closely.
"You look tired, Luce. Stick out your tongue."

She did as he asked.

He frowned. "Just as I thought. Coated."

She tugged out of his grasp and scrambled across his
legs to look in the old mirror that hung above the sofa.
Sticking out her tongue, she examined it with a frown,
then turned toward him. "My tongue is certainly *not*
coated. I'm fine."

He angled his head as though critically examining her.
"Are you sure you feel okay? You look washed out."

She plopped down on the bed beside him. "That's not
very flattering."

His lips quirked as he turned back to his work. "I
wasn't aware that you wanted me to flatter you." He
flipped a page over, giving it his full attention.

Lucy glowered at him, then got back up on her knees
and checked herself in the mirror again. She squinted,
tilted her face left, then right. "Washed out? You
think?" He didn't respond, and when she faced him
again, he seemed to be deep into his work. "Jack?" He
reached for a pen on the side table and made a note in

the margin, then picked up a calculator. "Jack?" she repeated more loudly.

"Hmm?" He didn't look up, but went on with his calculating.

She heaved a sigh. He wasn't even listening! This wasn't like him. Deciding she didn't appreciate his indifferent treatment, she scooted over and jabbed him in the ribs. "Jack!" she repeated.

He jerked, twisting around. "Hey." Giving her a narrowed look that was more amused than annoyed, he grasped her wrist. "Have you forgotten? I retaliate."

She smirked at him. "I dare you."

With a quick grin, he swept his papers aside. "You asked for it."

When she made a halfhearted attempt to escape, he snagged her around the waist. She squealed and struggled even though they both knew her plan had been to get caught. Jack tugged her against him, tickling her ribs. "Jack!" She slapped at the hand curled around her waist, crushing her back and hips against him. "Let go of me—you..." She couldn't go on when a fit of giggles burst from her lips.

"Are you going to poke me again?" he demanded playfully as she wriggled.

"Yes!" she cried, laughing. "When you ignore me, I'm going to poke you *hard*." With his renewed tickling, she yelped, kicking and squirming until she found herself twisted around to face him. "Don't do that! I'm going to poke you again—Jack—*quit*!" Instead of poking, she pressed her arms against his warm chest. "You're cruel."

"You started it."

"You're a brute," she shot back, laughing.

Suddenly, he was no longer tickling her, and Lucy found herself staring into beautiful cinnamon eyes that had gone serious.

They were breast to chest, almost nose to nose, and Jack's arm was hugging her close. The hand that had been tickling her now cupped her side—the fingers moved, splayed, the sensation caressing. Her flesh prickled beneath his touch and her heartbeat skyrocketed, making her breathing harsh and uneven. She grew alarmed and flustered by the unanticipated tension that suddenly surrounded them, crackling and snapping in the air like static.

She could tell that Jack felt something, too, for she saw him swallow hard. He opened his lips to say something, but hesitated. Lucy focused on those lips, thinking how nicely formed they were, remembering how expertly they could kiss....

Footsteps on the stairs drew their attention. "Oh, Jack! Telephone!" Elissa called. "I'm bringing you the portable."

Lucy was the first to react. Pushing away, she scrambled to the other side of the bed and hopped off. Embarrassed for them both, she was still struggling to steady her shaky limbs when Elissa burst through the basement door and rounded the corner.

The redhead stilled when she saw Jack in bed. "I hope, darling boy, that you have pants on under there," she teased. "I run a family establishment."

Jack grinned at her, his expression so carefree and commanding that Lucy couldn't be sure she'd actually seen uncertainty in his eyes only seconds before.

He took the phone from Elissa's fingers. "I'm sure whoever's calling has a great mental picture of me now. Thanks."

The redhead covered the receiver. "It's a woman, so I bet you're right." She handed him the telephone, asiding to Lucy, "She has a real low, sexy voice."

"Hello?" he said, then smiled broadly. "Why, hello, Desiree." His tone grew velvety and he looked at his watch. "It must be after three o'clock in Paris. What are you doing up?"

Elissa caught Lucy's attention and mouthed, "She's French," then waggled both brows suggestively when Jack chuckled at something the caller said.

"Of course I remember that night," he murmured, and Lucy was struck by the seductive quality of his voice.

What on earth was the woman on the other end of the line reminding him of? It sounded as though she must have said, "*Remember, darling, when we swam naked under the moon and you made wild, kinky love to me all night long on the beach?*"

Lucy was riveted there, unable to move, watching Jack's face, his sexy, crooked grin, his eyes, glittering with what she could only describe as desire. *Desire for a woman whose very name meant desire!* She wondered if this person on the phone was the fabled woman of his dreams. If she had come to her senses and—

"Luce?"

She started, blinking. "What?"

Jack indicated her bedroom with a nod. "This is personal. Do you mind?"

She felt a strange surge of dejection. "Oh—I'm..." She swallowed, backing away. It didn't occur to her until that second that Elissa was already gone. She felt like a fool, eavesdropping. It was utterly unlike her. With a weak smile, she backed into her room.

As the door closed, he was chuckling that deep, lusty chuckle, and the last thing Lucy heard was "I miss you, too, darling..."

Alone in her room, she leaned against the door. So Jack had a girlfriend. A *Desiree*. She *would* have a name like Desiree. She *would* be a sultry-voiced, sexy Frenchwoman—probably one of those anorexic model types. A beautiful, worldly, independent, uninhibited woman—a woman Jack professed to miss, one who was bold enough to call and remind him of wild sex games and who could flavor his laughter with provocative innuendos.

She felt a surge of—something—and squelched it. Chewing on her lower lip, she inhaled deeply and winced, realizing Jack's scent clung to her. She recalled his lips again and how close she'd been to them—how her mind had drifted to thoughts of—of...

She jerked away from the door, pushing the ridiculous idea from her brain. This woman phoning Jack from France was a good thing, she told herself. Jack deserved happiness. He was one of the most wonderful people she'd ever known. Why shouldn't he have a Desiree?

''That's great, Jack,'' she whispered as she scanned the shelves along her wall that held all the collection of angels he had ever given her over the years. Fingering the pin she wore, she wondered what sort of jewelry Jack gave Desiree. *Probably not angels*, some imp in her mind insisted on chiding. He probably thought of Desiree in a much more *earthy* way.

''That's very—uh—really *great*....'' she murmured.

CHAPTER SIX

ON SUNDAY afternoon, the family gathered in the parlor. Stadler stood before the fire wearing a Cheshire-cat grin. Lucy knew trouble when she saw it, and that smile spelled disaster.

At two o'clock, the inn was quiet since the guests checked out by noon and new arrivals weren't expected until four. This last day of March was sunny, with a refreshing nip in the breeze, the faint breath of a dying winter. Wood smoke and baby powder scented the air as a fire flickered low on the hearth. Worry tightened Lucy's stomach. What did Stadler have on his shrewd, obstinate mind?

Half-blocking the fire, he stood, his hands clasped behind his back, his legs braced wide, as though he was about to give a soliloquy. His eyes were on her and Jack as they sat, holding hands, on the sofa. Lucy tried to ignore Stadler's piercing stare and concentrated on watching Helen and Damien play with the twins.

Elissa sat in the leather chair to Lucy's left. Sareena paced somewhere behind the sofa. At least that's what it sounded like.

"Staddie?" The pacing stopped. "Staddie, I thought we were going to Mutton Hollow this afternoon. When are we going?"

Jack leaned close to Lucy, whispering, "I give her a nine point seven in Olympic whining."

Lucy's lips twitched at his joke. She found his attentiveness pleasant, considering how he'd dismissed her last night when Desiree called. Her fledgling smile faltered when she remembered the passion in his voice, his sexy laugh, his sleepy-lidded eyes while he talked with his lady love. *Desiree*. She wondered why that thought had come to mind and why it made her feel restless.

"Ena-pet," Stadler said, his smile and regard never wavering from Lucy, "we'll leave soon. I already told you we'd stay for the musical review—"

"But, *Staddie*," Sareena broke in, moving to him, fanning a brochure in his face, "there's so much cool stuff. It says here it's a little village in the woods—like a hundred years ago—with *real* cobblestone streets. And they make baskets and dip candles and you can learn to make apple butter and pig skins."

Stadler glanced her way, looking dubious. "They make footballs?"

Sareena laughed, a high-pitched, squeaky sound. "No, silly." She waved the brochure at him again. "It says right here that pig skins are a tasty snack food. And there's bluegrass music, too," she hurried on, appearing unbothered by his lack of enthusiasm. Grabbing his hand, she squirmed from one foot to the other. "You know how I love bluegrass music!"

He removed his hand from her two-fisted hold and patted her shoulder. "In a minute, pet. I don't want to miss the big announcement that Jack and Lucy are about to make." He transferred his glance from his petulant fiancée to Lucy. "Surely you have an announcement—while the whole family is gathered together." He looked from Lucy to Jack and back to Lucy, his lips lifting in a knowing smirk. "I'm amazed that you allowed me to be the first to know."

Helen and Damien glanced up from their places beside the baby blanket. "What announcement?" Helen asked as one baby girl batted at her mother's fingers with both tiny hands.

Lucy felt like giving Stadler a stern look, but instead, she shifted to stare at Jack. He grinned down at her as though the idea of making "an announcement" was exactly what had been on his mind. "Think we should, sweetheart?" he murmured loudly enough for all to hear. Before she could ask what he was talking about, he leaned closer, his lips grazing the shell of her ear, the touch stilling her. "The jerk is calling our bluff, Luce," he whispered. "We have to do this. Now, *giggle*."

Though Lucy was taken aback by what he said and agitated to think the lie had to go one step further, she allowed a frothy gurgle to escape her throat. It sounded almost genuine.

Before Jack moved away, he nipped at her earlobe, his echoing chuckle deep and sexy. She didn't realize her eyes had gone wide until they felt dry and prickly. Her pulse doubled, tripled, and a tingle skidded along her spine that made her shiver. Jack was good at this being-engaged stuff. That little nip at her ear did very peculiar things to her metabolism.

Partly to embellish on the falsehood and partly because she was irritated at him for the erotic-teeth thing, she gave him a firm nudge in the ribs. "Oh, Jack, you're so *bad*," she scolded, her eyes telegraphing her *real* meaning, while the grin of a lovesick loon rode her lips.

Casting a glance at Stadler, she was rewarded with a dimming of his cheeky smile. Maybe it was worth taking the lie to this new, inconceivable plateau just to see that.

"What announcement?" Elissa asked, sitting back and tapping her nose with the rattle she'd been using to entertain Little Elissa Two. "Do you two know which twin is named for me?" Her expression was a burlesque of excitement, as though she knew that couldn't be the announcement. The remark was calculated to get Helen and Damien to tell her what she wanted to hear.

Jack laughed. "You have a one-track mind, Elissa. That's not the only announcement in the world."

Elissa sat back, looking put out. "It's the only *important* one."

"What is it?" Helen asked as she picked up one fussy baby to snuggle.

Jack lifted Lucy's hand and kissed her knuckles. When he did, their eyes met, and Lucy was awed by the tenderness she saw there. The emotion seemed so honest she could almost believe it herself. Except for Desiree, of course. "We've decided to get married next Saturday," he said.

For some reason, Lucy couldn't help but smile back. Jack was cute when he lied. His cinnamon eyes twinkled with warmth and humor. Her knuckles still tingled, a keepsake of his kiss. She amended her thought. Jack was cute, *period*. And the touch of his lips could cause a feminine reaction no matter which miscellaneous body part he aimed at. *Knuckles, for heaven's sake!*

"Of course you two are getting married next Saturday," Elissa said, her shrewd lawyer face set. "I knew that already." She shifted to look at Stadler. "You weren't the first to hear." Making a production of turning disdainfully away from him, she faced Jack and Lucy and smiled. "My darling sister asked me to be her maid of honor. Didn't you, sweetie?"

Lucy opened her mouth to speak, but Helen added, "And she asked me to be her matron of honor." She touched Damien's thigh. "Here's the best man." She threw her husband a kiss, which he caught and put in his pocket over his heart. Swinging toward Lucy and Jack, Helen looked quite believable when she asked, "Who didn't know?"

Lucy smiled, amazed at her sisters. When they decided to carry out a fraud, they were amazing. She blessed them both. Surely, seeing how casually they all accepted the fact that Lucy and Jack were going to be married in a mere six days, even Stadler would get the idea and go. She lifted her chin and tossed her ex-fiancé a look that asked, "Who's got egg on his face now?" Resisting the lure of Stadler's sensuality seemed easier when she was safe in the midst of her family—and good, solid Jack was holding her hand.

"Staddie?" Sareena tugged at his sleeve. "I think I'll take my guitar. It says here they let guest performers wander the streets and play for free." She smiled around at the rest of the gathering. "I'll have a chance to perfect my style." She shifted to look at Lucy and Jack. "Oh, and congratulations. You're very cute together."

"You noticed that, too," Jack murmured as the small woman sprinted from the room.

"What exactly *is* Sareena's style, Stadler?" Elissa stood, straightening her skirt, the rattle in her hand accompanying her movements. "No, don't tell me." She tossed the toy onto the white baby blanket. "I'll read about it in the morning paper." She straightened, then made a sweeping move in the air with her hand. "I can see the story now. 'A woman was pelted to death with apple butter and half-woven baskets after an impromptu concert at Mutton Hollow caused outraged visitors to take up arms in self-defense. No charges have been filed. According to police officials, the incident is being called "justifiable homicide".'"

Stadler's expression grew hateful. "What has Sareena ever done to you, Elissa?"

"Why—she found *you* attractive, of course." Kneeling, she gave each of her nieces a kiss. "I'd better check with Jule to see if the room's ready for the Wilsons. Ta-ta." At the parlor door, she turned back. "Oh, by the way, Jack. There's a three-day waiting period for getting married here in Branson, so you two had better get on down to the courthouse and apply for your license in the next day or so."

Jack grinned. "Yes, Mother."

As the tall redhead disappeared, Sareena dashed back, panting, her guitar case clutched in her hand. The image of a grunge rocker in slashed jeans and flannel shirt, the petite brunette had added a new accessory. A nose clip. And there was a pink streak in a section of her hair that stood straight up between her eyes. "Ready, Stad?"

He gave his petite fiancée a tolerant smile. "Coming, Ena-pet."

"Will you two be checking out in the morning?" Lucy looked around in alarm, shocked to discover the question had come from her own lips. And worst of all, she'd sounded panicked. The idea of going to the court-house and actually—well, she didn't want to go that far. Was it against the law to apply for a marriage license when you had no intention of getting married? *Maybe never in your whole life*? She just wanted Stadler to leave, give her the time she needed to think, to heal. She didn't want to go around applying for marriage licenses.

At her tremulous question, Stadler turned. "Leave? Tomorrow?" His sandy brows rose as though the idea had never occurred to him. Lucy held her breath, expecting the worst, but hoping for a miracle. "Actually, the season is just starting here for many of the performers, and Sareena can learn so much about country and mountain music from watching them." He smirked at Lucy—the smirk of a snake, if a snake *could* smirk. "And I've been wanting some quiet, out-of-the-way place to work on a play I've been tossing around in my mind. I don't have to be back at the university until May. I think this place would be perfect."

Lucy felt groggy from lack of oxygen. He couldn't have said what she thought he'd said. He couldn't mean he planned to stay—*until May*! No, surely he would go with Sareena to wherever she lived—hopefully on another planet.

"Naturally, I wouldn't want to miss your wedding, Lucy-pet." Stadler gave Jack a speculative look. "I certainly wouldn't want to miss that."

Jack squeezed Lucy's hand, clearly communicating that she must be brave, hold on. "That would be—nice," she mumbled.

"I knew you'd be happy, Lucy-pet." Stadler's conversational tone didn't fool her. *The sarcastic jerk!* "And since this is the slow season in Branson, Elissa can use the extra money, I'm sure."

Jack sat forward, but didn't relinquish her hand. "We could make it a double wedding, Tinsley." He grinned. "What about you and Sareena joining us at the altar?"

Dismay jolted through Lucy, but Jack's hold tightened, warning her not to strangle him just yet.

"Staddie!" Sareena squealed. "Could we? Oh, it would be killer to get married in this cute town."

Stadler's smile disappeared. When he turned to his animated fiancée, he almost, but not quite, recovered his pleasant expression. He grasped her pointed chin between his thumb and forefinger. "Remember, Ena-pet, you said you wanted a big church wedding. And your mother's wedding dress needs altering. You have so much family in St. Louis." Lifting the hand from her chin, he slipped the nose clip from her nostril and tucked it into his jacket pocket. Shaking his head, he appeared almost fatherly. "You wouldn't want to deprive your parents, all your aunts and uncles and your three sisters from sharing your joy. You'd never forgive yourself."

Sareena's face fell. "Oh—oh, Staddie." She shrugged bony shoulders, her features pinched. "We'd be mean to do that. You're right." She took his hand. "You're always right." Turning toward the door, she tugged. "Let's go, *Stad*-muffin."

Once they were gone, Lucy pulled from Jack's hold and vaulted up to glower at him. "How could you sug-

PLAY

"ROLL A DOUBLE"

AND GET UP TO

FIVE FREE GIFTS!

HERE'S HOW TO PLAY:

1. Peel off the label from the front cover. Place it in the space provided in the coupon to the right. With a coin, carefully scratch off the silver dice. Then check the claim chart to see what we have for you – up to four books and a gift – ALL YOURS! ALL FREE!

2. Send back this card and you'll receive specially selected Mills & Boon® romances from the Enchanted™ series. These books are yours to keep absolutely FREE.

3. There's no catch. You're under no obligation to buy anything. We charge you nothing for your first shipment. And you don't have to make a minimum number of purchases – not even one!

4. The fact is, thousands of readers enjoy receiving their books by mail from the Reader Service™. They like the convenience of home delivery and they like getting the best new romance novels at least a month before they are available in the shops. And, of course, postage and packing is completely FREE!

5. We hope that after receiving your free books you'll want to remain a subscriber. But the choice is yours – to continue or cancel, any time at all! So why not accept our no-risk invitation. You'll be glad you did!

You'll look a million dollars when you wear this lovely necklace! Its cobra-link chain is a generous 18" long, and the lustrous simulated pearl completes this attractive gift.

ENLARGED TO SHOW DETAIL

THE READER SERVICE : HERE'S HOW IT WORKS

Accepting the free books and gift places you under no obligation to buy anything. You may keep the books and gift and return the despatch note marked "cancel". If we don't hear from you, about a month later we will send you 6 brand new books and invoice you just £2.30* each. That's the complete price - there is no extra charge for postage and packing. You may cancel at any time, otherwise every month we'll send you 6 more books, which you may either purchase or return - the choice is yours.

*Prices subject to change without notice.

THE READER SERVICE™
FREEPOST SEA3794
CROYDON
Surrey
CR9 3AQ

▼ DETACH AND RETURN THIS CARD TODAY. NO STAMP NEEDED! ▼

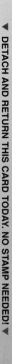

gest that we have a double wedding? That would have been tough to fake!''

He relaxed back, looking up at her. ''It was a bluff, Luce. I didn't think he'd take me up on it. I thought he might face the fact—''

''You *thought*?'' She smacked his knee hard. ''You do way too much thinking, pal!''

Helen laughed, placing her fretful baby daughter against her shoulder. ''Okay, so now that we have a wedding to plan...'' She indicated Jack with a nod and gave Lucy a look that said, ''*Don't you want to tell him that you two are destined to marry*?''

Lucy gasped at the silent, dangerous message. She dropped to her knees beside her sister. ''Don't you *dare*, Helen!''

''Dare what?'' Jack asked.

Damien only chuckled.

That night, Lucy was on her way downstairs to her room when she caught sight of Elissa pacing in the reception hall. ''Anything wrong?'' she asked.

Elissa spun around, looking strung out. ''Oh, it's you.'' She sagged against the reception desk. ''I was waiting for Stadler.''

Lucy was startled. ''Really? Why?''

In an uncharacteristic show of vulnerability, Elissa swung her tortured gaze to her younger sister. ''I can't stand it any longer. I can't stand having him here making you miserable. It's gone too far. I never thought we'd have to plan a wedding! I'm going to demand that he leave. First thing in the morning.''

Lucy was amazed and felt a tingle of hope. Could this awful farce end in the morning with Stadler's departure? She didn't know how they'd get out of the wedding thing, but she knew Jack would think of some excuse. ''But, Elissa, isn't this sudden?''

The redhead took hold of her sister's shoulders. "Not a bit. I've been so upset for so long. I've tried to hide it, but I can't put you and Jack through this any longer. I—" At that second, the door opened and Elissa whirled to confront Stadler as he and Sareena came inside. "You have to go, Tinsley," she said in a rush. "I want you out. *Tomorrow morning*!"

Lucy stood transfixed, expecting to see Stadler go all red in the face, to bluster and argue. But he didn't. He merely leaned against the door and smirked. "I don't think you really want that, Elissa."

Lucy watched her sister pull herself up to her full height. "I own this inn and I insist that you leave. You're only paid up through tonight, and—"

"That's where you're wrong."

Elissa stopped in midsentence, frowning. "What do you mean?" she asked, her tone dubious.

Lucy became concerned, too. Stadler was a wily man. What did he have on his crafty little mind?

He strolled over to the reception desk, lounging an elbow on it. "You'd better check your receipts. Yesterday, that Jule person was manning the reception desk. I believe she said you were in town on business. Anyway, I paid her for the rest of April."

Elissa visibly paled as Stadler's triumphant grin broadened.

"As an ex-lawyer, you know you can't easily get me out of here. I haven't done anything wrong and I've paid for the room. At least," he added, his smile going hard, "I wouldn't recommend that you try." He took Sareena's hand and tugged her toward the staircase hall. "Come Ena-pet. It's been a long day."

Without a backward glance, he and his baffled-looking fiancée disappeared upstairs.

"Elissa?" Lucy managed in a weak whisper. "Is he right?"

Her features ashen, Elissa slowly came out of her trance and blinked forlornly at her sister. "Oh, I could fight him. But by the time it got through the system, he'd be gone anyway, and he knows it. He also knows I don't have the time to deal with the paperwork and taking him to court. And worse, he'd sue. I simply don't have the money for that." She heaved a gloomy sigh. "I—I'm sorry, Lucy. I should have kicked him out right away. I—I just didn't think he'd be such a pig."

Lucy squeezed her sister's shaky fingers. "It's not the end of the world," she murmured, trying not to sound as despondent as Elissa looked. "We'll get through this."

Elissa blinked back tears. "You're a good person, sweetie." She hugged her hard. "I don't deserve you."

Lucy hugged her back, but couldn't force words past the lump of despair in her throat. All hope for a reprieve from this mess was gone for good. The fake marriage was on.

Lucy felt as though she'd been poleaxed. In a daze, she carried the faxed newspaper article up the stairs to Helen and Damien's room. She knocked and her younger sister let her in. "Hi…" Helen stopped speaking, her expression closing in concern. "Good grief, Lucy. You look like you've just watched your best friend get hit by a bus."

Unable to put words to her thoughts, Lucy held out the fax.

Helen took it, scanned the article, then wide-eyed, looked at her sister. "Wow!" She turned toward Damien, lounging on the bed, feeding one of the twins. The other baby slept beside him. "Look, honey." She handed him the fax. "It seems that the news of Lucy and Jack's upcoming wedding has hit Kansas City. One of Elissa's law school friends faxed this."

Damien read the article, then handed it back, sending Lucy a grin. "Looks like it's news when a rich restaurateur like Jack Gallagher gets a marriage license."

Lucy sank into a straight-backed chair near the door. "I had no idea this would happen." She pressed her fists to her temples, hoping it would ease the pounding of her head. "This is terrible. Terrible!"

"It's not so terrible, Lucy." Helen came over to pat her sister's arm. "It's fate. After all, Jack's your destiny, and—"

Lucy grabbed Helen's arms and shook hard. "Don't you ever—*ever*—breathe a word about that myth to him, do you understand? First of all, Jack has a girlfriend. He told me himself that he loved somebody, and I saw it in his eyes when he whispered to her on the phone. So don't mention that myth in front of him." When she realized she was hurting her sister, she dropped her hands. "Forgive me. I know you and Damien believe in the D'Amour myth because of the way you met and all, but—but, well…"

She shook her head, vaulting up, needing to pace. Stalking the length of the Victorian room, she spun to face her sister. "I'm not even sure I believe in love anymore. I hate Stadler, and yet, sometimes…" Her lips began to tremble with memories, and she had to work to get herself under control. "I don't know my own feelings because of him. He—he's made it hard for me to—to trust. To believe in…" She swallowed hard. "Look, Helen, Damien, I might as well say it out loud," she cried. "Marriage isn't in my vocabulary anymore. I don't know if it ever will be."

The door creaked open and they turned to see Jack standing there, his expression troubled. He peered down the hallway, then stepped inside and closed the door. "Declare that any louder, Luce, and the jig is up," he admonished in a whisper. "Stadler's coming down the hall."

Lucy hurried over to him, horrified. "What did you hear?" she demanded. The last thing she wanted to do was embarrass Jack with that foolish myth story.

He took her hand and led her away from the entrance. "Shush," he cautioned. Putting a finger to his lips, he cocked his head as though listening. A door down the hall banged shut. He faced her then, releasing her hand. His brow knit. "Luce, please make sure the door is closed before you start shouting about how you don't believe in marriage."

She frowned back, her jaw working. It didn't look as though he'd heard anything about the myth. He was only concerned about the marriage lie. She nodded, embarrassed. "I—I will." She remembered the newspaper article, and her anger flared. Looking around, she spied the sheet of fax paper on the floor. Dashing over, she snatched it up to show him. "We have bigger problems right now. Read this."

He gave it a cursory glance. "I've heard. My secretary called. It's in the New York papers, too."

Lucy felt as though he'd just dropped a hot rock into her stomach, and she groaned. "This is great."

"I'm sorry," Jack said quietly.

She gave his chest a petulant shove. "Why do you have to be rich and famous anyway?"

Damien chuckled. "Life can be a bitch."

Lucy glared at her brother-in-law. She knew his opinion about the myth and hoped her bloodthirsty look told him to keep out of it. With a renewed chuckle, he turned back to feeding his daughter.

"Look, Luce." Jack took her hands. "There's no problem. We can announce that it will be a private ceremony here in the inn. Period. No press allowed."

With his encouraging smile, she couldn't stay mad at

him. After all, this new problem was causing him more difficulty than her. He was the famous one. She managed a weak smile. "What are you going to tell Desiree?"

His brow furrowed, and Lucy didn't blame him for being upset. She took his hand. "If you'd like, I can talk to her. Assure her—"

"No," he interrupted, "I'll talk to her."

Knowing she was leaping wildly off the subject, but unable to stop herself, Lucy asked, "Is Desiree the one, Jack? The one you loved and couldn't have?"

He eyed her dubiously. "Why do you ask?"

She shrugged, having no idea why. "Just curious. I only thought—from the way things sounded the other night on the phone—that maybe you were getting somewhere with her."

He studied her for a long moment, unsmiling. She waited, feeling off center, wondering why she wanted his answer to be—no. Wondering why she wanted him to tell her that Desiree was a passing fling, merely a way to ease his masculine libido.

After what seemed like an eternity, he nodded. "Let's just say I'm working on it."

Her mood dipped. For some reason, she didn't think she liked Desiree. She didn't think the sexy French confection was good enough for him. Jack wouldn't be happy with some driven, bony, self-centered nymph. He needed a solid, sensible woman. One who would make him a cozy home, give him two or three children with laughing cinnamon eyes and—

"Is something wrong, Luce?" he asked, breaking through her musings.

She started, blinking to bring him into focus. A terribly arresting presence, he stood there, tall, broad shouldered, his scent pleasantly male.

"Uh—no, I—that's just *great*," she managed, holding on to her smile.

Jack's love life was none of her business.

*   *   *

"You don't have to sew that button on my shirt, Lucy," Jack said as he thumbed through his business faxes and the mail, pretending that Lucy's nearness wasn't driving him mad with longing.

She looked up from her perch on the couch that served as his bed. She wore soft-looking jeans and a short-sleeved pink sweater. Her feet were tucked beneath her. He drank her in as desire surged through him. He wanted to take her in his arms, make love to her, but he kept his expression impassive.

"It's my pleasure," she said. "You know I love to sew."

He couldn't help but grin. "Well, it's nice of you, but not necessary. The laundry usually does it for me."

"Not while I'm around." She wet the end of a piece of thread. Though he struggled to ignore her, when she puckered up like that it was damned hard. After she lowered her glance to thread the needle, he forced himself to look away. Staring blankly at the mail, he couldn't seem to register anything but her nearness. Pretending disinterest to her while she sat so close to him was damned near impossible.

The phone rang. Elissa had moved it to the table beside the couch when Jack started getting daily calls from Desiree.

"Jack," Elissa shouted from the top of the stairs, "it's for you."

"Thanks." He picked up the receiver. "Hello?"

"Well, Jack," said a familiar male voice on the other end of the line, "what's this I hear about you getting married?"

Jack cringed at this unexpected complication. "Well, well. This is a surprise," he said, trying to sound nonchalant.

"Jack?" Lucy asked tentatively.

He looked her way. "Just a second," he said into the receiver. "Yes, Luce?"

"Is this private?"

He shrugged, nodding. "That would be better."

She bit off the thread and laid the shirt beside him. "All done anyway. I'll go up and see the twins."

Once she'd left and the basement door clicked shut, Jack turned his attention to the phone. "Nate Broom. It's good to hear from you, man. Is there a problem with the sports equipment I donated to your church?"

Nate laughed. "Nope. Everything's great. And I don't know how much credit you deserve, but the gang crime in my neighborhood is down by twenty percent since your stuff came. I think, between your money and my sweat, we're going to turn some of these inner-city kids around. Say, when are you dropping by to hear one of my hellfire sermons?"

"Next time I'm in Chicago. Count on it. How's Maggie?"

"Maggie's wonderful. Starting to show. Our third's due in July. But don't get me off the subject. You're in big trouble, buddy. I can't believe you thought you could get married and not have me perform the ceremony. I'm hurt, fella. I'm sitting here bleeding." Though Nate didn't sound all that devastated, Jack knew his friend would naturally expect him to officiate.

The two men went way back. They'd met as kids in juvenile hall after some minor scrapes with the law. Both of them had had some good luck come into their lives—by way of male helping hands—or they might have turned out very different people. "Look, Nate, it's not that I don't want you to—"

"Don't bother explaining, Jack. I'll forgive you when I get there. There's only one hitch. It's Thursday. I'm taking some of the kids on a camp-out, but I can catch a flight out of Chicago on Saturday morning. So, good buddy, as sure as the sun shines, expect me for the ceremony.''

''But, Nate—''

''Oh, and congratulations. I know how long you've loved her. I'm happy for you, man. I'll see you soon.''

''But, Nate, I—''

The phone went dead. Jack mouthed a curse. Nate had one tiny flaw in his character. He didn't let you finish a sentence. Jack wondered how he counseled his flock. Probably told them to get their heads straight and shut up.

He closed his eyes, his chuckle ironic. Well, once he explained the situation, Nate would understand. The trip wouldn't be a total loss. They'd get to see each other.

Absently, he began to shuffle through the mail. His consciousness caught on the name ''Damien Lord'' and he realized Jule had mixed Damien's mail with his own. Suddenly restless, he pushed off the couch and headed up the basement stairs.

Before he reached the door to Helen and Damien's room, he could hear voices. The door stood ajar. He ran a frustrated hand through his hair, then exhaled with relief when he remembered that this evening Stadler had taken Sareena to Mel Tillis's opening show of the season. There was no danger of her suspicious ex-fiancé overhearing anything he shouldn't.

As he drew nearer, he heard Helen say, ''But, Lucy, I don't agree with you. Jack has a right to know about the myth.''

Deciding it wasn't gentlemanly to eavesdrop, he knocked even though the door lolled half-opened. Smiling, he asked, ''What myth?''

Helen and Lucy looked up from where they were standing over the double baby stroller that served as the twins' bed. Both women stared at him, looking as though they'd been caught with their hands in his wallet.

Helen recovered first. "The door wasn't closed, was it?"

He shook his head, coming in. "I brought up this letter for Damien. Where should I put it?"

Helen indicated the bedside table. "There's fine. He'll be back in a minute." She cast Lucy a worried glance that intrigued Jack.

"What's going on?" he asked. "What myth do I have a right to know about?"

Lucy was still frozen in her bent-over stance, staring at him, her eyes wide and somehow frightened. She straightened, slanting her sister a narrowed look.

Helen covered the sleeping babies, then she, too, straightened. "I'm not supposed to tell you, Jack." She went to the bed and sat down on it, crossing her arms. "So my lips are sealed."

Confused, Jack looked from one sister to the other. "Luce?"

She swallowed hard, her cheeks pinkening to match her sweater. "It's nothing."

He lifted a disbelieving brow. "If it's nothing, then it can't hurt to tell me."

Lucy's shoulders were stiff, her hands clasped before her. She turned away.

Jack grew worried and faced Helen. "My Lord, is somebody sick?"

Helen squinted at her sister, looking put out with her, then she returned her gaze to Jack. "Lucy, I'm sorry, but I think fate brought him up here. He has a right to know."

Lucy spun on her sister. "A letter brought him up here! Jule's dyslexia brought him up here! That's all!"

Helen harrumphed and got off the bed. She went to Jack and took his hands in hers. "Jack, it's like this.

There's a myth about the D'Amour mansion. It states that any woman who sleeps there, under a full moon, on her birthday, will be destined to marry the first man she sees after she wakes up.'' She squeezed his fingers and cast a quick, fretful glance back at her sister, who stood stone-still, looking out the window. "Lucy slept in the mansion, under a full moon, on her birthday, and you were the first man she saw.'' She heaved a big sigh. "There. It's out. I feel better.'' She released Jack's fingers and went back to perch on the bed. She squinted at Lucy. "So hire Elissa and sue me.''

The blonde whirled to face Jack. "Ignore her. She's lactating. Her hormones are all haywire. She doesn't know what she's saying.'' Looking as though she wanted to die, Lucy brushed past him and hurried from the room.

"Oh, heavens, Jack. That look on your face,'' Helen said. "I've done a bad thing, haven't I?''

Jack glanced at her, not sure what to think.

"You look awful.'' She clutched her hands together. "Lucy said it would embarrass you, but I thought—I mean, with the marriage thing going this far, I felt in my heart it was fate, and—and...'' She stopped, bit her lip. "Well, that's how Damien and I met. We *believe* in the myth.'' She shook her head, running her hands distractedly through her hair. "Have I done wrong, Jack?''

The magnitude of Helen's revelation had stopped him cold, like a club to the back of his head. He frowned, shocked. Loving Lucy the way he had all these years, he'd been willing to go along with a fake wedding, knowing she wasn't emotionally ready to hear of his love. But now, now that Nate was on his way to marry them, and now that he knew about the myth...

Damn! Did he have to get bashed in the head with it before he knew this marriage was right? He loved Lucy with all his heart and soul. They had a legitimate marriage license, and a real minister was coming to officiate. It had to be right. *Had to be fate*! Lucy simply wasn't ready to see it yet.

The inevitability of it filled the air like a high-voltage current, lifting the short hairs at his nape, constricting his ability to breathe. Did he dare go through with the insane plan his heart was aching for?

''Jack?'' Helen asked cautiously.

He glanced her way, still scowling. Feeling a mixture of shameful guilt and heady satisfaction, he simply stared at her, his body rigid with tension.

''Say something,'' Helen whispered, looking as though she was afraid if she spoke too loud he might explode.

He worked his jaw, coming to a hard-fought decision. Damien had said it almost a week ago. Lucy *would* discover she wanted him as much as he wanted her. Jack just had to do his part.

After all, hadn't he just discovered that he was her destiny?

A pressure in his head, in his chest, told him his emotions were still warring, making him feel unsure that he had any right to do this. Suddenly, he seemed to be standing on the sidelines, watching himself, as he turned to fully face Helen.

With a degree of disbelief, he heard himself say, ''I forgot to mention, I found somebody to play the part of the minister. He'll be perfect.''

CHAPTER SEVEN

IN A daze, Lucy stared into the murky looking glass over her dressing table. When she'd bought the cream linen fabric she'd made this jacket dress from, she'd had no idea it would become her wedding gown. Well, her wedding gown for her *fake* wedding.

Absently, she fingered the gold-and-diamond angel pin on her lapel, fretting that the above-the-knee hem was shorter than she might have preferred for a wedding dress. *Fake wedding dress*, she amended glumly.

She sighed, shaking her head at herself. The tiny diamond stud earrings that had been her mother's winked at her earlobes. She had pulled her hair back, capturing the willful stuff as well as she could in a turquoise clip. But unruly tendrils fell about her face, stubbornly defiant of being tamed. She only wished she had the same, go-to-blazes spirit as her hair. That might make this fraud easier to deal with. Heaving a despondent groan, she turned away from her grim reflection.

Her room was relatively dark for late afternoon since she'd been forced to pull the drapes across the slice of basement window set high in the wall. Media photographers were gathering like flies, threatening her privacy as they attempted to snap pictures of Jack Gallagher's elusive bride-to-be.

"You about ready?" Elissa called, tapping on her bedroom door. "It's nearly four o'clock."

Exhaling forlornly, Lucy stepped into the beige pumps she'd borrowed from her older sister. "I guess."

She walked to the door feeling as though she were going to the gallows. How could her pride have gotten

109

her into such a huge, horrible lie? She wasn't even sure if it had been *her* pride, or possibly Elissa's, or even Jack's somehow. She didn't have that much ego. So how was it that she was pretending to get married today, and that tomorrow the story would be splashed across newspapers all over the country? The whole idea was absurd. But at this point, there wasn't much she could do about it. Except make fools out of them all—especially Jack. And she wouldn't do that. What a headline that would make.

Besides, she couldn't stand to see her ex-fiancé's triumphant grin if he discovered his suspicions had been correct all along. He'd stayed at the inn for exactly that reason—hoping to prove the whole thing was a pride-saving lie.

Darn Stadler's Machiavellian hide.

When she opened her door, she expected to see Elissa, but instead, Jack was looming there. She caught her breath. She'd never seen him looking quite so—so dangerously attractive—somehow predatory, though there was no overt sign of it. He looked so laid-back and casual, she had no idea where that absurd notion had come from. His hands were plunged indifferently into his trouser pockets, and he was grinning down at her.

Clearly his dove gray cashmere jacket and black, raw silk trousers were of designer quality. His shirt was black, with one of those non-collars that looked almost clerical. There was an attitude about his attire that was bold yet classic, strong yet quietly seductive.

"Hi," he said. "How are you doing?"

The sound of his voice brought her out of her momentary trance and she asked, "What—what are you doing here? I thought the groom wasn't supposed to see his bride before the…" She realized she was being silly and laughed self-consciously. "I'm sorry. I keep forgetting."

"I thought you might need some bolstering." He took her hand. "Besides, I don't believe in bad luck. How do you feel?"

"Terrible." She laced her fingers with his, shaking her head. "Don't you?"

He glanced away, his smile gone. "Yeah, in a way." When he looked at her again, he gave her a wink. "But I have a feeling it will work out."

She inhaled to calm herself. "I hope you're right." She had a thought. "Is your actor friend here?"

"Yes. He knows what to do." Jack tugged her toward the couch. "Why don't you sit down? You seem shaky." She followed him without argument and sagged onto the squeaky cushion. He joined her, placing an arm around her shoulders. "You look nice, Luce." His breath was soft against her cheek.

She glanced his way, her smile sickly. "Sure. Me and my sale-table linen and you in your Gianni Versace chic."

He laughed, his embrace tightening. "How'd you know that?"

She frowned. "I've read a few *Gentlemen's Quarterly*s in my day."

"Well, my taste in women's clothes runs to Lucy Crosby chic." He squeezed her affectionately, and she couldn't help but smile. Shaking her head at him, she let out a low laugh. "What's funny?"

She shrugged. "I was just thinking, Jack. I don't know if I could have gone through this with anybody but you." Her cheeks grew hot, and she knew she must be blushing. "Especially after what Helen told you about the myth." She touched his thigh with fondness, but thought better of leaving her hand on his leg. The brief contact with the solid, male muscle, even sheathed in fabric, made her palm tingle. She hurriedly replaced her hand in her lap. Her fingers fidgeted among themselves, and she lowered her gaze to stare absently at the nervous dance they were doing.

"I feel the same way, Luce. I could only do this with you," he murmured.

And somehow she believed him. Jack was so dear. There were very few men who would have gone this far for a friend. But the Crosby sisters knew he would crawl through fire for them. He was certainly proving that now.

"This will be a good experience," he added. "I've always told you I'd only marry once."

"So this is good practice?"

He tucked a knuckle under her chin and tipped her face up, forcing her gaze to meet his. "Practice makes perfect."

His grin did odd, unruly things to her heart and she felt a surge of gratitude. Her dour spirits lifted slightly. Still, she couldn't help but ask, "How did—did Desiree take all this?"

He was quiet for a long time. His expression grew thoughtful, his eyes narrowed as though perturbed. After another moment, his gaze slid to hers and he flashed a wry grin. "She's fine with it. Desiree is a very open-minded woman."

Lucy absorbed the news with misgivings. She didn't know if such open-mindedness was a positive thing in a relationship. "I'd think she'd be angry. I know I would be."

He looked squarely at her. "Really?"

She looked away, concentrating on a crack in the faded floral wallpaper. "Well, darn it, Jack. You deserve a woman who can't stand the idea of your being in another woman's arms. *Kissing* another woman—even as a favor to an old friend. I'm not sure..." She stopped, bit the inside of her cheek. What did she think she was doing, giving Jack advice on his love life?

"You're not sure—what?" he coaxed.

She peered at him, miserable and not sure why. "Well—it's just that…"

Her mouth worked, but before she could form her thoughts, Elissa came into the basement. "Okay, you two lovebirds. It's time to put on this little clambake." The redhead looked striking in her hunter green coat dress. Its slim fit accentuated her figure, the rich color complementing her fiery hair.

She hurried to the couch and reached out as though she expected them each to take a hand. When they didn't, she bent and grabbed them. "By the way, Jack, where have you been hiding Nate? He gets here and *whoosh*, you lock him away in one of the attic rooms. I know actors are odd, but…" Elissa tugged them up on their feet. "Is he going over his lines? I hope he doesn't muff this deal. After all we've been through."

Jack gave her a quick hug. "He won't, little mother. I guarantee it." Taking Lucy's hand, he squeezed her fingers reassuringly. "I'll see you upstairs."

He walked away, grace and supple elegance marking every step. She watched him disappear around the corner.

"Hirk's so excited." Elissa's comment drew Lucy's gaze. "He's popping his buttons with pride that we asked him to give you away. He even bought a new suit." Lucy felt a stab of regret that their friends had to think this farce was the real thing. She gave her sister a pained look and Elissa patted her cheek. "Real wedding or not, Hirk's having a great time. He needed the suit anyway." Grabbing Lucy's hand, Elissa propelled her toward the stairs.

Lucy's mind whirled and tumbled as the ceremony began. The wedding seemed so real. She watched in awe as the fake Reverend Nate Broom spoke of the sacredness of marriage, of loving, trusting and moving through life's trials, caring for each other and working to keep their union strong and solid.

A marriage ceremony should be such a sacred thing, not this awful sham. She felt so unhappy about what she was doing, tears shimmered in her eyes. She knew her bouquet of pink roses and baby's breath was shaking badly, but she didn't dare look down, fearing a guilty tear would escape.

The scent of roses filled the parlor. Damien and Helen had been sweet to provide the bright sprays of flowers that adorned the room, and to think of her bridal bouquet and Jack's boutonniere. The parlor was transformed for the wedding, the furniture pushed against the wall to make room for a semicircle of white folding chairs with an aisle down the center.

Nate Broom stood before the hearth, now cleared of ashes and filled with a bouquet of white roses. To Lucy, the actor looked like a real minister. In his golden robe, black cassock and clerical collar, he was marvelously realistic. Except for his hair, which was a little long and shaggy for her idea of a pious man of the cloth. Still, his voice rang out, rich, deep and passionate, as he asked the questions about loving, honoring and cherishing.

Lucy did the best she could, keeping her ''I do'' clear of the trepidation and dejection she felt. But when Jack spoke the vows and gazed at her, she felt strangely better. He smiled at her, his eyes telegraphing a tenderness and a strength of purpose that lifted her spirits.

She had no ring for him, but when it was his turn, he slipped a wedding band on her finger. Simple, elegant, golden. She blinked down at it, then at his face. Somewhere off in the distance, she thought she heard the words, ''You may kiss the bride.''

Shifting to stare at the actor, she questioned with her eyes. When he nodded, she was sure the blood had drained from her face. *The wedding kiss*! She'd forgotten about The Wedding Kiss. Memories of the *other* kiss they'd shared came roaring into her brain. She cast Jack a helpless glance, but was met by those cinnamon eyes, calming her, telling her to trust him.

He leaned close, his lips brushing hers, then he moved slightly away. This time, it was his turn to silently question her with his eyes. He was telling her that he wouldn't do anything to upset her or rattle her, and somehow she knew that was true. Suddenly, she wanted him to kiss her again and felt herself leaning in his direction. Oddly fearless, she lifted her hands to his shoulders and drew his face to hers, gifting him with a kiss.

He accepted the boon with restraint, his mouth moving tenderly against hers. It was curious how, this time, the touch of his mouth was almost like a dream. Vaguely sensuous, elusively thrilling, but just out of reach somehow. His hands stroked along her back, coming to rest at her waist, yet there was nothing demanding or lustful about his touch. When he lifted his face away, she felt sweetly drained, curiously deprived. And a little dizzy.

Taking her hand, he led her down the aisle and whisked her into the basement.

"Whew," he said, looking slightly flushed. "How do you feel now?"

She didn't know what to say. She felt warm. "Was it hot upstairs to you?" she asked.

His grin held a cryptic element. "I was hot."

She fanned herself with her bouquet. "I thought it was awfully warm, too—there toward the end." Indicating her room, she said, "I guess I'd better get changed."

"Right. We want to be on the road as soon as we can."

She had reached her door, but wheeled around, confused. "On *what* road?"

He half grinned. "Didn't I mention it? I made reservations in Eureka Springs, Arkansas."

"What for?"

He shrugged off his jacket, slipping his hands into his pockets. "What would Stadler think if we didn't go on a honeymoon?"

She frowned at this new development, then peered at him, shaking her head. "Why not?" she muttered. "While we're at it, maybe we ought to have a few kids?" She wasn't sarcastic often, but for some reason she couldn't stop herself from blurting that. She flinched, immediately sorry.

Jack lifted a skeptical brow, his smile slow and sexy. "I'm not sure Desiree is that open-minded."

For once, Lucy had to agree with Jack's French girl-friend. If *she* were Desiree, she certainly wouldn't want Jack Gallagher going around having babies with...

Her cheeks sizzled at the vision that leaped to her mind—of Jack and *her*, tangled intimately together in Eureka Springs sheets.

"Anything wrong, Luce?" he queried, his voice low and smoky.

"No! *Nothing!*" She spun away and slammed her door between them.

Lucy vowed that before she left on this so-called hon-eymoon, she was going to have to wash her mind out with soap.

She quickly changed into white trousers and a short-sleeved sweater. For luck, she transferred the angel pin to her going-away outfit. As the couple returned upstairs, Lucy scanned Jack. He'd changed into navy trousers and a light blue shirt, and she felt a strange measure of pride in how handsome he was. Without dwelling on why, she took his hand, drawing his gaze and a surprised smile.

The reception went by in a blur and was coming to an end. Jack and Lucy circulated, visiting with guests. Luckily, Jack had had the presence of mind to suggest that wedding gifts be made in the form of donations to their friends' favorite charities. So at least one good thing had come from this mess.

Maybe *two* good things, she mused, catching Stadler's frown. She snagged his glance and gave him a superior smirk. Instead of this discouraging him as she'd expected, he moved away from the cluster of people beside the dining-room table and ambled toward her, where she was standing near the stairs. She sucked in a nervous breath and cast around for Jack. He was idling near the front door, deep in conversation with Hirk Boggs and Nate. She couldn't get his attention.

Instinctively, she headed his way, but Stadler caught her arm before she'd made three steps. "Lucy—Lucy," he said in that deep, beguiling tone he used so effectively. He smiled, and that darned dimple appeared. She felt a flutter in her stomach and wasn't sure whether it was foreboding or appreciation.

"What is it, Stadler?" she asked as crisply as she could.

He took hold of her upper arms, stepping into her space. "'I am a man more sinned against than sinning.'"

She was puzzled and grew irritated. One thing about Stadler she had never loved was his propensity for making a point by quoting Shakespeare. Most of the time she was lost. "What do you *want*, Stadler?"

He grinned again, evidently sensing her unease. He had the instincts of a jungle cat, able to smell fear. His cunning smile altered before her eyes to become the expression of a reproachful parent. "What you're doing is foolish, Lucy-pet."

She panicked at his accusation, frightened that he'd figured out the ruse.

"This is a rebound romance. It won't work. You're deluding yourself if you think it will."

She had opened her mouth to defend the lie, but thank heaven he'd been true to form and barged on ahead. Clearly, he didn't have any proof that the marriage was a fake. His ego was talking again. She inhaled, managing a smile. "I don't know why you should care, Stadler." She indicated his new fiancée with a nod. The petite woman was easy to spot with her pink stick of hair and her bright purple dress that looked like it had been fed through a shredder. Lucy noticed that the young woman no longer wore her nose clip. Apparently, Stadler had removed it again. "You have Sareena," she reminded him.

He gave his fiancée a cursory glance, then his plum eyes settled on Lucy, his gaze intent. "Lucy, I'm forced to admit something to you," he said in an agonized whisper. "I love you, but I can't *afford* you." He gritted his teeth, inhaling through them. "Don't you understand? Sareena's daddy is a wealthy man. He's promised to fund the play I'm writing. I'll also star in it. I didn't want to have to admit all this. I didn't think you'd go to such lengths to try to stay away from me." Looking tormented, he shook his head, his eyes closed. Lucy wondered how much of it was an act. "Don't you see?" he insisted in a low moan. "Sareena is my ticket. She wants to be a singer, so I'm here keeping her happy, working on my play when I can." He stopped, swallowed visibly. "And wanting you desperately—because you are my true love."

"I don't believe you," she cried, her heart pounding. She was disgusted by his admission. Part of her believed him, but part of her thought it was just another lie to keep her dangling. "You're terrible, Stadler."

"A man does what he must in this life, Lucy-pet. The world isn't always fair to lovers." He cupped Lucy's chin in his hand. "I know you love me, and one day you'll come running back to me. People can enjoy each other without marriage. You know what Shakespeare says about—''

''Nope, Tinsley, and we don't give a damn.'' They both turned at the sound of Jack's voice as he closed in on them. ''Here's a quote for you, old buddy.'' He took hold of Stadler's arm and firmly separated his hand from Lucy's face. '''The cost of living is going up and the chance of living is going down.''' Releasing his grip on Stadler's arm, his lips curled in a deadly grin. ''Flip Wilson said that. And I'll prove he was right, at least where you're concerned, if I ever catch you insulting my wife with your unwanted attentions again.''

Stadler recoiled, rubbing his arm. ''I was not insulting her.'' He turned to Lucy, scowling. ''Was I, Lucy-pet?''

She stared at Stadler's calculated expression. It was as though he was telling her she *had* to defend him. Fury burst to life inside her. How dare he? How dare he think he still had such a hold on her? She glanced at Jack, who was watching her. She thought she saw hope in his eyes. The look stirred something in her and she swirled back on Stadler. ''Yes—yes, you *were* insulting me.'' To emphasize her irritation, she popped him in the stomach, drawing a groan. She didn't wait around to see his expression. Taking Jack's arm, she tugged him away.

He chuckled. ''I thought I was the only person you punched.''

''I made an exception in his case. He was being a total jerk. You wouldn't believe what he said.'' Her face blazing with a mixture of guilt and liberation, she peeked at Jack. He was grinning at her. ''Besides, I was afraid if I didn't punch him, you would.''

His chuckle rang again, strong and deep. ''The lady reads minds.''

The pleasant sound was infectious, and she smiled, towing him farther away from Stadler to a place where they were alone. ''I need to say goodbye to my sisters,'' she whispered, "then we'll go. And thanks." She didn't add that she wasn't sure what she might have done if he hadn't come along. The touch of Stadler's hands, his passionate vow of love, still had a baffling effect on her emotions. She seemed to teeter between wanting to strangle him and—and... She cursed herself. *Would she ever get her head on straight again?*

Jack surveyed her in silence. It seemed as though he understood her emotional turmoil. He squeezed her hand. "Thanks for your thanks, Luce." Releasing her, he added, "I'll get our interference ready."

He started to walk away, then paused, his glance connecting with hers again. His lashes drifted down like dark lace as he scanned her hair and her face. A heartbeat later, he lowered his head, closing the distance between them. When his lips settled against hers, any rational thoughts she might have had dissolved into dreamy bits. Though his kiss was brief, Lucy experienced an intimacy in the deed that stunned her.

As he straightened, he slipped his hands into his pockets, his grin wry. "For show," he explained under his breath, then left her to go about his task.

After a dull-witted couple of heartbeats, Lucy regained herself and hustled Elissa and Helen into the kitchen, giving them each a hug. Elissa laughed. "And thanks for aiming your bouquet at my face. It was either catch it or be blinded. But I don't see myself getting married any time soon. I'm too cantankerous for most men."

Lucy kissed the redhead's cheek. "You're too much woman for most men. I have a feeling the right one will come along one of these days."

Helen reached up to smooth back a stray hair from Lucy's face and tuck it behind her ear. "You have a good time, you and Jack." Her smile was almost sad.

"I still think…" She shrugged, crushing Lucy in a tight hug. "Well, you know what I think."

Once Helen had stepped away, Elissa took Lucy's hand and led her toward the party. "It's time for us to help you and Jack sneak out." She gave her sister a wicked grin. "And if anything—happens—between you two in that town, so famous for honeymoons, don't fret about it. Watching you up there exchanging vows, even *fake* ones, I thought you kids made a perfect couple."

Elissa had never been particularly romantic, so her little speech was wildly out of character. Lucy shook her head, grinning. "I feel better with your permission. My plan was to rip Jack's clothes off at the very first stop sign."

With her sisters laughing, they reentered the party where Jack and Damien were coaching the guests in the escape plan.

The scheme worked perfectly. Hirk was tall like Jack, and with his coat held up to mask his homely face, and with well-wishers crowding around, throwing blinding amounts of birdseed at the media, they managed to keep the press safely away. Nobody could swear it wasn't Jack getting into the hired limousine.

Jule covered her face with a scarf, even though no one knew what Jack Gallagher's new bride looked like. So, after the armada of press followed the limo out of the drive, heading on their red-herring trek to Springfield, Lucy, Jack and Nate scrambled into Hirk's butter-and-egg truck. Nate got up front and drove into town while Jack and Lucy pressed close together in the windowless back.

As they hopped out of the truck at the prearranged parking lot, Nate trotted around to meet the couple. He was grinning from ear to ear, and Lucy was struck again by how nice-looking he was. Shorter than Jack and with dark blond, shaggy hair, he had a muscular football player's build. He stretched out a hand. "Jack, you old dirt-bag." After the brief handshake, he pulled his friend into a bear hug. "I've been praying for this day for a long time." He stepped away from his friend and gave Lucy a big, satisfied grin.

She smiled back. "I'm sorry we didn't get to visit, Nate," she said. "But I want you to know I think you're very good."

His brows lifted. "Why, thanks." He winked. "The woman has taste, but you always said so." He squeezed Lucy's shoulder. "Someday we'll have to sit down and have a nice long visit about this lunk you—"

"That'll be fun, Nate," Jack cut in. "But right now, your cab's here. You don't want to miss that flight, man."

Nate gave his friend a shrewd look. "Oh, sure, *I'm* the one in a hurry." He laughed, then gave Lucy a kiss on the cheek. "Be happy, you two."

Jack picked up Nate's knapsack and shoved it at him. "Go!" he ordered.

As the shorter man loped toward the waiting cab, his bass laughter filled the air.

Lucy watched him go, then waved as he headed out of town toward Springfield and the airport. When she turned to Jack, he was watching her. She made a doubt-ful face. "Be happy? He sounded like—"

"Method actor," Jack mumbled, turning to get their bags. "Nate puts himself into his roles. A little nuts, but a good friend."

Lucy nodded. "Oh. Well, whatever, he was really convincing, wasn't he?"

Jack set their bags on the pavement and closed the back of Hirk's truck. "He convinced me," he said with-out making eye contact.

He indicated his rental car, parked not far away, and

Lucy had to give him and Damien credit. They'd worked out their escape with flawless precision.

"Let's go, Mrs. Gallagher." This time he looked at her and grinned. Hefting their bags, he headed toward the car.

She smiled, joining in the game. "Okay, but there's just one thing—Mr. Gallagher."

He put down the suitcases beside the car trunk and faced her. "What's that?"

"I've never been on a honeymoon before," she teased. "What does one do?"

He propped a hip against the back of the car, scanning her with amused warmth. "*One* does very little, but two..." He wagged his eyebrows mischievously, and even in the face of such outlandish suggestiveness, she found herself laughing.

Naturally, he was kidding her with the sexual innuendo. There was his French girlfriend, Desiree, to consider. Still, for some crazy reason, Lucy couldn't think of an argument that could make her rethink this trip with Jack to one of America's quaintest honeymoon spots. When he opened her door for her, she slid inside feeling more contented than she had in a long time.

Now that the reality of the situation was staring her squarely in the face, Lucy thought she could come up with *one* argument against the trip. They were sharing a room.

Jack had explained it, though. What if somebody called? he'd said. Lucy had left a number in case of emergencies. That meant Stadler could check on them. Two rooms would give them away as surely as an admission on the front page of the newspaper.

Some time later, Lucy yawned in spite of her anxiety. The day had been long and stressful. She'd napped on the fifty-mile drive along curvy country roads, among the forested rolling hills, but she didn't get any real rest. Thankfully, their dinner had been waiting for them in their room—a tray heaped with luscious varieties of breads, meats, cheeses, fruits and a tasty gourmet coffee. Even faced with the epicurean repast, Lucy hadn't been hungry and had only picked at the food.

"Do you want to take the first shower?" Jack asked, breaking into her troubled thoughts.

She snapped around to look at him. "Me?" she squeaked.

He lounged in a tufted velvet chair beside their dining table, which was tucked into the huge bay on the far side of their room. He appeared relaxed, his hands resting on his knees. He looked right at home, a little over-size for a turn-of-the-century room crammed with lace, fringe and curios, but otherwise, right at home. At her high-pitched question, he canted his head, his grin growing inquisitive. "Aren't you the one I'm honeymooning with?"

Her cheeks burned and she felt silly. After all, he hadn't suggested that he join her. "Oh—uh—sure. I guess."

She had busied herself unpacking when they'd first arrived, so she scurried to the cherry armoire with beveled-mirror doors, gathered her toiletries and an oversize T-shirt and escaped to the bathroom. Thirty minutes later, she was combing and fluffing her hair, standing on the room's second-floor wraparound veranda. The view she had was the inn's secluded back lawn, complete with an English-style garden with winding stone paths and discreet lighting. A gurgling fountain, strategically lit, was resplendent as the garden's centerpiece.

The night was surprisingly warm for this time of year. She inhaled the fresh air, smiling at herself, at her foolish, momentary trepidation. After all, this was Jack.

As if on cue, the bathroom door clicked open, and she

turned, her smile fading. There he stood, dressed in nothing more than a towel, once again looking too male for a room awash with cabbage rose and wisteria chintz fabrics. He stopped when he noticed her standing there, her comb stalled halfway through her hair.

"Jack—what—what…"

He grinned at her and ambled across the polished floorboards to lounge against the doorjamb. "I think it's called a towel, Luce."

She scanned his bare chest, still glistening with water droplets that twinkled amid a light matting of chest hair. Swallowing hard, she leaned all of her weight back on her bare heels. Against her will, her gaze roamed lower. She gulped around the lump forming in her throat. The towel seemed insufficient, he was such an imposing presence. And his legs, bare and powerfully built, were long and bronze. Her mind chided, *Jack has legs that are exactly what a man's legs ought to look like.*

There was movement as a muscle bulged in his thigh. Lucy gathered that he was shifting his weight from one foot to the other. Her gaze lifted, but she winced when she discovered she was focusing on the towel again. As he moved, there was the trace of—of…well, areas beneath that towel that were extremely anatomically correct, and she shouldn't be staring.

"I forgot to get any shorts." When her gaze skittered to his face, he was half grinning at her. The golden light that filtered up from the garden spotlights gave his eyes a mysteriously lethal quality. "I usually sleep in the raw," he said. "Sorry."

She swallowed, or at least tried to. Her throat had gone dry. He looked so lazy, so nonchalant, leaning there in the doorway, which wasn't fair somehow, for she had gone as stiff as a board. "No problem," she finally wheezed. Then she went on combing her hair. He nodded and turned away. She watched for a few seconds, agitated. With effort, she finally forced herself to turn her back on him.

He padded across the Oriental rug. The click of the bathroom door told her he was safely out of sight. But she didn't turn, didn't reenter the room. She kept combing and fluffing like an automaton, her thoughts on a subject far more disturbing than personal grooming. After another few minutes, when she heard the bathroom door open again, she found herself needing to turn around. To savor him with her eyes.

This time he was wearing a pair of dark blue shorts. Even though they were baggy and almost reached his knees, they hid all too little of his bothersome anatomy. He went to the closet and took down a folded blanket. Flipping it open, he laid it on the floor.

"What are you doing?" she asked.

He didn't face her, but folded the blanket in half on the dark pine planks. "Fixing up a bedroll."

She frowned. The wood was hard and the blanket was thin. "You'll get all stiff."

With a chuckle and a shake of his head that she didn't understand, he straightened to look at her. Her confused frown was a wordless request for an explanation, but he only shrugged, his grin fading. "Look, Lucy. You can't be suggesting that we share the bed."

She blinked. Of course she wasn't suggesting such a thing. It wouldn't be decent. After all, he was a man and she was a woman. "Well…I suppose…"

He winked at her in understanding. "Don't worry about it, Luce. I can handle the floor. Just because you climbed into my bed a hundred times when we were kids, doesn't mean we could share a bed now. I mean, how can a man and a woman sleep together and—" he lifted a shoulder nonchalantly "—just sleep? That's what you're thinking, right?"

He went about his work, gathering up one of the pillows from the bed.

"Just sleep?"

He looked at her, his expression charmingly candid. "What?"

She rolled her comb nervously between her hands. Was she being ridiculously Victorian? After all, this was Jack. Why deprive him of a good night's sleep simply because he was a man? Didn't she believe in equal rights? "I'll sleep on the floor," she said.

He eyed her dubiously, as though she'd said she planned to eat worms. After a second, he shook his head. "Not likely, Luce. Not while I'm around."

She gave him a perturbed pout. "Okay, then, *you* won't sleep on the floor while I'm around. How do you like that?" He stared at her for a long moment. She watched as disquiet seeped into his eyes, and she wondered if he realized it was there. She smiled this time. Really smiled. "I won't attack you, Jack. You can trust me."

His own grin was slow in coming, but when it came it was dazzling. She guessed that it was that very same smile that had knocked many a panting female off her feet. She sucked in an appreciative breath at the sight.

"You're sure you don't mind?"

She shook her head, startled at her sudden inability to form words.

Picking up the pillow, he tossed it back onto the bed. "Thanks." He refolded the blanket and returned it to the closet shelf. Then with a yawn, he reached for the bed coverings. "I think I'll turn in, then." She watched as he folded back the crocheted spread, then crawled beneath the mauve blanket. He reached for his bedside light, then stopped. "I'll let you get in before I turn it off."

She dropped her comb, then stooped to pick it up,

fumbled for a second before she could manage to grab it. "Uh—sure…" Walking like a zombie, she headed to the opposite side of the antique bed.

Its headboard was a piece of art in itself, with luxuriant carvings of cherubs and roses. But right now, she wasn't in the mood to admire the furniture. She laid the comb on the diminutive marble-topped commode on her side of the bed. When she glanced over at Jack, he smiled.

Tentatively, she smiled back, plucking up the corner of her covers and sliding beneath them. "I'm in," she whispered. The light was doused and she felt him move. "What are you doing?" she squealed.

"I'm turning on my side." There was silence for a moment before he spoke again. "Luce, are you sure this is okay with you?"

She could tell by his voice that he was facing away from her, and she bit her lip. How stupid could she be? What did she think was going to happen? *After all, this was dear, trustworthy Jack.*

CHAPTER EIGHT

JACK waited, listening for the sound of her breathing to slow, grow even. After an hour of the torture of being so near her, straining not to move a muscle, he was finally sure she was sleeping. With infinite care, he shifted to his back, turning his head so that he could watch her.

His breath hitched. She looked even more angelic in repose. The soft light filtering up from the garden paid homage to bone structure that was dainty, feminine; her features were almost ethereal. Fine blond hair lay tousled across her pillow, and his fingers itched to—to... He bit back a curse, knowing he should turn away, but his need for her was too overpowering to heed the dictates of his brain.

His gaze roved hungrily to her mouth, just full enough to drive a man wild. Her lashes lay across her cheeks, looking like silver on porcelain, and he battled an urge to run his tongue across them, to kiss the milky lids of her eyes.

With a shudder, he gave himself a stern order to look away, but his eyes disobeyed, lovingly scanning her face—memorizing every curve and hollow. Her skin was flawless, like cream, and he was in agony for a taste. He inhaled a sharp breath, trying in vain to squelch his frustration. Nothing did any good. His gut throbbed with unquenchable desire.

Hell, this was his wedding night. He was in bed with the woman he had loved most of his life, and he couldn't show her, couldn't tell her all the things locked in his heart. She would hate him forever if she found out about his unscrupulous deception. *And, damn him, he wouldn't blame her.*

Almost from the first moment he'd arrived in Branson, he'd been manipulating her. He hadn't known it would go this far, would never have started all this if he'd known.

But it was too late to begin again. She was a married woman now. His wife. Only she didn't know it. His original strategy had been to make her want the very thing she was. Unfortunately, now that everything had gone this far, that strategy was all he had left. So he had no choice but to go through with it.

Tonight, when he'd come out of the bathroom wearing a towel, he'd thought he'd seen a faint spark of hunger in her eyes. The sight had so overwhelmed him, it took all his strength to keep from rushing to her, dragging her into his arms and making crazy love to her right there on the veranda. But somehow he'd managed to pretend nonchalance, to make do with recalling that tiny beginning of passion in her gaze.

And now that memory gave him hope, even made him eager to forge ahead with his plan. He was in her bed. A miracle—or possibly the biggest mistake of his life. He choked back a blasphemy. What a damnable position to be in. He never intended to be a paper husband. He wanted to be a real flesh-and-blood lover, to show her they were meant for each other, body and soul.

Yet he couldn't risk moving too quickly, no matter how he burned to know her fully. He would wait and watch. Pretend not to care as he looked for the signs. He knew Lucy loved him. She'd told him so. He could only trust that before long, she would also *want* him the way he wanted her.

He just had to do his part.

She moved, suddenly facing him. When she snuggled with her pillow, he experienced a torrent of raw, mindless jealousy for that bag of feathers. Her lips parted slightly as though in invitation, and he stifled a groan of longing. She might look like an angel, but she was a natural temptress. Even sound asleep she could blow him apart.

As he drank her in, watching her sleep, he felt his control faltering. This past week, while he'd pretended indifference to her nearness, his ability to restrain himself had been superficial at best. And now he could sense his hold slipping to dangerous levels. Unable to help himself, he turned on his side to face her, but gradually and with excruciating care, so he wouldn't wake her and frighten her.

The slender hand on her pillow twitched, as though beckoning. He glanced from her fingers to her face. Serene and lovely. Closing his eyes, he sent up a prayer, asking that he be forgiven his weakness. His feelings for Lucy were too mighty to keep bottled up inside any longer. With great reluctance and guilt, he lifted himself up on one elbow. *Dammit. This was his wedding night. At the very least, he had the right to kiss his new bride. Didn't he?* Leaning across the short distance that separated them, he placed a feathery kiss on those lips he cherished, lips that rode his dreams hard and made him wake up in a sweat.

He didn't dare allow the touch to linger, yet when he drew away, he couldn't retreat to his side of the bed. He put it off. Even knowing the risk of delay, he remained there, inhaling the clean scent of her hair, the sweet aroma of her skin.

Her hand moved again, and she made a small sound that in the quiet affected him like a scream, almost giving him apoplexy until he realized she was dreaming. The rapid eye movement behind her lids made that obvious. Relieved, he soundlessly settled down to watch her, wondering what she was dreaming about. Her lips lifted in a smile that sent spiky shards of lust ripping through him. He reached out to her, then caught himself, pulling back his hand, fisting it.

"Luce, darling, I hope you discover you love me," he whispered roughly, "before you find out what I've done to you."

Lucy woke up feeling toasty warm, a nice change from the chill she'd felt during the night. She stretched, then frowned, confused. She seemed to be confined. Had she twisted herself up in the blankets trying to get warm?

"Morning," came a deep voice, so close it reverberated through her body.

Her eyes popped open and she stared around. She was in bed, but she wasn't lying where she should have been. She squinted, groggy and disoriented. Wasn't that her pillow over there—empty? And if that was the case, and she was on Jack's side of the bed, then where was…?"

She jumped as the realization hit her sleep-dulled brain. Twisting around, she found herself staring into Jack's neck. She shifted to look up. He smiled at her. "Morning," he repeated. "Sleep well?"

She pushed herself up on one elbow so that she could stare down at him. "What's going on? Why am I—I…?" She swept an arm over them, unable to put her question into words.

"Why are you snuggled against me?" he helped, still grinning an infuriating grin, as though the sleeping arrangement was more amusing than outrageous.

She pushed up to sit. "Yes. *Why?*"

He came up on an elbow. "You tell me." He gave her a wry look that included one lifted brow. "I didn't move."

She swallowed. The fact that she was practically crowding *him* off the bed was so apparent, her cheeks sizzled. For some reason, she felt the weirdest sense of depression about that.

"Were you cold?"

"Cold?" she repeated absently. After a second, the question penetrated. *Cold.* She had been; she remembered now. Suddenly, she felt stupid and her affront drained away. With a weary shake of her head, she smiled. "I was cold. I'm sorry. I hope I didn't make you uncomfortable."

Though a swift shadow of something indecipherable flashed across his features, his smile didn't waver. "To be honest, you're very comfortable to sleep with."

She was surprised how her initial embarrassment vanished with his teasing compliment. "Thanks a bunch. I'll add it to my résumé."

It startled her when she found herself smoothing his sleep-tossed hair back off his forehead. Jack had the softest hair. The dark fringe of his eyelashes went up a fraction, as though he was startled by the intimacy of her touch.

She grinned down at him. "You know, you're pretty cute in the morning."

"I'm darling," he said with a chuckle. "I thought that was already in my résumé."

She laughed. "I guess I missed it."

He shifted slightly, but not away from her. Just so that he could see her better. "Are you sure you want to get up? It's early."

She had an urge to sink back into the toasty blankets and curl up beside him, maybe even place her arm over his broad chest and hug him close. Did she dare? Quite unexpectedly, a feeling of extreme impishness came over her. She leaned across him supposedly to better see the bedside clock. "What time is it?" she asked, not a bit interested.

She thought she heard the tiniest groan as her breasts

brushed against him, but when she peeked at his face she couldn't decipher his expression. He was watching her through shuttered eyes.

Quickly shifting her glance back to the clock, she murmured, ''Seven-fifteen.''

''Early,'' he repeated.

She sighed and stretched. ''You're right. Maybe I will catch a few more minutes of sleep.'' She gave her side of the bed a provoked glance. ''But it's cold over there.''

When she looked back at him, his grin was wry. ''Want me to go over there and warm it up?''

She felt a flash of irritation at his thickness and inhaled deeply. ''No, don't bother. I thought I might— stay here....''

A dark brow rose as though the thought hadn't occurred to him. ''Oh? Sure. If you want.'' He turned on his side, patting the bed. ''I'll keep you warm.''

She felt a reckless surge of excitement, but her conservative upbringing made her pause. ''You don't think it's wrong of us?''

His jaw worked for a second, and Lucy feared he was trying to be polite, not wanting to hurt her feelings even if he did think her idea was terribly inappropriate. That would be just like Jack, wanting to spare her feelings. He was so nice. But even if that was the case, she couldn't seem to draw away.

''Luce...'' he finally began, sounding slightly hoarse. ''The important question is, do you think it's wrong?''

She shook her head, not knowing why she was behaving so rashly. But something deep inside her seemed to be insisting this was utterly right. Sinking to the mattress, she pressed her backside against him, wondering if he would think the move wanton or just a search for warmth.

She was startled but pleased when his hand snaked around her waist. ''Warmer now?''

"Mmm-hmm."

"Sleepy?"

"Mmm-hmm," she lied. Jack's nearness, his soft breath ruffling her hair, his scent all around her, were far from sleep inducing.

She put her hand on his, and he automatically laced their fingers together. His heart beat hard against her back. Or was it her own heart pounding her rib cage into dust?

"Lucy?" he asked after a few panicky minutes.

"Yes?" she whispered, breathless, anticipating something but not knowing what.

"I—" The ringing of the phone stopped him from finishing whatever he was going to say. After the second ring, he pulled his fingers from hers. "Excuse me," he said, a tinge of exasperation in his words. "Probably business."

He reached for the receiver, propping himself up on a pillow and leaning back against the headboard. She shifted so that she could watch him, wondering who was calling at this hour—*interrupting their honeymoon!* She blanched at the asinine thought as he said hello. What was wrong with her brain this morning?

His expression changed, grew wry, then a devastating grin spread across his face as the person on the other end of the line spoke. Lucy knew before he even said her name that his beloved Desiree was calling.

"No, you didn't wake me, *ma chère*," he murmured, his voice going velvety. "I was just lying here thinking about you." There was a pause and he chuckled. The hair on the back of Lucy's neck stood up at the sound— so naughty, so full of innuendo. Her cheeks began to burn.

Jack briefly shifted to glance at Lucy, then he said something into the receiver in French. It had to be dirty. There was no way anything spoken in *French* in that

low, suggestive tone could possibly have meant ''How's
your mother's lumbago?''

She touched Jack's hand, and darn him, a full half
minute lumbered by before he acknowledged her. ''One
second, *ma chère*,'' he finally said, then covered the receiver, looking at Lucy. ''Desiree thinks we have sepa-
rate bedrooms. You understand. Whisper what you
want.''

Lucy squared her shoulders, feeling somehow
slighted. ''Sorry,'' she said quietly. ''I just wondered if
I should go?''

He winked at her. ''Go on and shower. Breakfast
should be up soon.''

She nodded stiffly and slid off her side of the bed.
Her walk to the bathroom was accompanied by more
deep, obscene chuckling and more *French*.

Once inside the bath, she stood beside the old-
fashioned claw-foot tub, pulling her T-shirt over her
head. She found herself stopping right in the middle of
the task, the fabric swathing her face. She inhaled. Jack's
scent had permeated her T-shirt. A great smell. Mellow,
masculine. She sucked in another deep breath, then another. Another. It wasn't until she'd made herself dizzy
that she realized how bizarrely she was behaving.
Standing in the bathroom, hyperventilating through her
T-shirt, for heaven's sake! Snatching the garment off,
she marched to the shower and flipped on the knobs.
Ducking under the cold spray, she gasped, welcoming
the discomfort and not wanting to think about why.

When she stepped out of the bathroom, her heart fell.
Jack was still on the phone. But he looked up at her and
grinned, indicating the table in the big bay window.
When she looked, she noticed that he was telling her
breakfast had arrived.

"Okay, Jane, fax them to me. I'll get back to you with my decision this afternoon."

She shifted to look at him again. He wasn't talking to Desiree any longer. Jane was his secretary. Suddenly, she was starving. The croissants, fresh fruit and steamy coffee looked delicious. With a lightness in her step, she hurried to the table and sat down.

Jack hung up and swung out of bed. "I'll take a quick shower and join you, but don't wait for me. I know how you get."

She had picked up a strawberry and was about to bite into it when she turned to him. "How I get?"

He laughed. "Have some coffee, grumpy. Just save me a little food, okay. I'm a growing boy."

"If we run out, you can always order more." She hiked her chin. "And for your information, I am a *delight* in the morning and I eat like a bird."

He stopped at the bathroom door, leaning a shoulder against the jamb. "I heard somewhere that hummingbirds eat their weight every day."

She rolled her eyes at him. "How much can that be? A few ounces?"

His rich laughter filled the room. "*Touché*. See you in a sec."

After he went inside the bathroom, she bit into the sweet strawberry and smiled. One thing you could say for Jack, he wasn't a grouch in the morning. As she chewed, her smile faded. Of course, if a man's hot-to-trot girlfriend calls and has phone sex with him when he first wakes up, it's bound to affect his mood for the better.

She swallowed, picked up another strawberry and bit into it without much interest. The vision of Jack and that—that other woman…well, it wasn't conducive to hearty eating. She shoved the thought away as she crammed the piece of fruit into her mouth.

Ten minutes later, Jack emerged from the bath, his dark brown hair damp and looking almost black. He wore a pair of snug jeans, but no shirt. "Anything left for me?" he asked as he padded barefoot to the table.

"Hardly a thing," she teased, since he could see the platter was still heaped with delicacies. "Aren't you going to put on a shirt?" She clamped her jaws shut, startled she'd said that out loud.

He'd sat down and was reaching for the silver coffeepot when she spoke. He glanced at her. "A shirt?"

She shrugged, smiling embarrassedly. "Never mind."

He frowned at her. "Does my bare chest offend you?"

She waved off the idea. "Of course not. You have a sexy chest. I mean, er, *no*, I'm not offended." She could feel her face glowing. What had possessed her to use the word "sexy"? "You're fine. Forget it."

"Sexy, huh?" He picked up the coffeepot and poured himself a cup. "I'm flattered."

"Oh, Jack!" Lucy felt stupid about her slip and floundered to neutralize it. "You know you have a great body. I'm sure this morning Desiree was reminding you of things you've done to her with your great body that would shock the civilized world." She cringed inwardly. Somehow, that statement hadn't been quite the neutralizer she'd planned.

"You give my body too much credit, Luce." He chuckled, lifting his cup to his lips. "But thanks."

She was mortified by his taunting and vaulted up, her brain spinning as she tried to think of something terse to hurl back at him. How dare he take what she'd said as a compliment? But before she could come up with anything that would wipe the crooked grin off his face, she heard a sound that drew her attention.

She turned. "Jack? Did you leave the shower running?" She looked at him as he set down his coffee cup.

He cocked his head toward the sound, seeming to hear it for the first time.

"I guess I did." He got up. "Don't know where my mind was." When he passed her, he gave her shoulder a squeeze. "I'll put on a shirt. We wouldn't want my body to worry yours."

She froze under his touch—not so much in reaction to his teasing, but more from the lingering sensuality of his fingers. Her breathing had gone haywire, too.

After he'd turned off the shower and donned a knit shirt, he resumed his seat at the table, swathing butter across his croissant.

"Jack?" She came up to him, smiling. It never took her long to get over being irritated at him. He was too darned easygoing. She was ready to spend the day sightseeing with him. "What do people do first on a honeymoon?"

He stopped buttering and slanted her a look that sent a tingle along her spine. What in the world had that look meant? He turned away without comment to stare out of the bay window at the shady lane that fronted their hotel. His jaw worked.

Feeling peculiarly flustered, she blurted, "I—I was reading in the hotel literature about local places of interest. Did you know there's a ten-foot-long piece of the Berlin Wall here? And there's a place called Cosmic Cavern not far away that has two underground lakes? I'd love to see that." She was babbling, she knew, but for some reason it seemed important to fill the silence with mindless chatter. "The Eureka Springs Botanical Garden sounds beautiful. And there's even a *frog* collection, of all things. That might be fun." Jack had gone back to buttering his croissant and didn't respond. "Er, speaking of fun, I was reading about a place called Quigley's Castle with *actual* trees, birds and fish all inside. It seems Elise Quigley wanted to sleep under big canopies of trees in full bloom, so—''

''That's nice, Luce,'' Jack interrupted. ''But it looks like I'm going to be busy today. With restaurant work.'' He looked up at her for a second before opening a tiny jar of plum preserves. ''I'm only going to have time for a quick bite before I have to go down to the hotel office and collect the work Jane's faxing me.'' He grinned easily. ''But you go. Have a good time.''

Her spirits flagged. ''By myself?''

He had turned away, but he looked back, his expression questioning. ''What?''

She didn't know why she'd thought they would spend this time in Eureka Springs together. After all, they weren't really on their honeymoon. And Jack was a busy man. He had gone way above and beyond the call of duty already.

She shook her head, smiling wanly. ''Nothing. Sure. I'll take the walking tour of the city. Did you know that the whole downtown is listed on the National Register of Historic Places in America? It'll be fun.''

''Did they bring us a newspaper, Luce?'' he asked as he spread preserves on his croissant.

She closed her mouth. *He wasn't even listening.* He didn't care about their spending time together. She gritted her teeth. Since he didn't, why should she? With a sigh, she pivoted and went over to the bed. She plucked up that morning's *USA Today*. ''Here.'' She dropped it in his lap, then slammed out the door.

At two o'clock in the afternoon, Lucy dragged herself back into their room and unceremoniously collapsed on the bed, her head landing at the bottom and her feet plopping onto the spread over her pillow.

Jack was lounging on his side of the bed, reading

through some business papers. He looked up as she threw herself down next to him.

"I'm dead," she moaned. "No wonder they call this town America's Little Switzerland. It's up and down, up and down. I feel like I've climbed the Alps."

She heard Jack chuckle. "Not enough time on the stair-stepper machine, huh?"

She swung her head around to look at him, or rather his feet. She scowled at them. Bare—and pretty darned cute for feet. "Well, at least *I* got some exercise." She shifted to look at his face. He was grinning at her. "You'll turn to flab, buddy, if you don't get off your—your—*whatever* from time to time." Mentally, she was facing the fact that it would take years for his well-toned body to show any signs of disuse, but she slapped the thought away, rushing on. "You can't work all the time, you know."

She couldn't figure out why she was snapping at him. After all, there had been nothing in their honeymoon agreement that dictated he had to keep her company. She was being childish. But even though she scowled at him like a reproachful schoolteacher, Jack didn't appear particularly chastised.

With a groan, she turned away, muttering, "My feet are killing me."

"Want me to rub them?"

She shifted back, eyeing him quizzically. "What?"

He shrugged. "Rub them." He cocked his head toward her feet. "I wouldn't mind. As a matter of fact, I'm a closet foot fetishist."

She drew herself up on an elbow to eye him better. "Very cute." She turned on her side to face him.

"No, really. Feet drive me wild." He wagged his brows. "Want to see?"

"Yeah, right." She lay back down on her stomach,

dismissing the idea. "Okay, have a party, pervert. Rub away."

She gasped when she felt her tennis shoes being tugged off. Rolling to her side again, she gave him a dark look. "Jack, what do you think you're doing?"

He held one of her shoes. With a wink, he dropped it to the floor. "Gettin' hot." A second later, her other shoe thudded to the floor. "Hand me your feet."

She frowned at him, but she knew her expression held more amusement than concern. "I will not."

His teeth flashed in a wicked grin. "I like feet that play hard to get."

She couldn't suppress a giggle. "*Freak.*"

"Foot freak," he amended, grabbing one of her feet and tugging off her sock. "Ah, the naked beauty of it all."

He gripped her ankle with one hand and ran a finger along her instep with the other, his expression as admiring as if her aching appendage were a rare orchid. "Jack, if you stick my toes in your mouth, I'll scream."

He slanted a laughing gaze her way. "I love a dare." With that, he bent to take her big toe between his lips, teasing with his teeth.

She squealed and pulled away, but he clutched her ankle too securely for her to break the hold. "Jack," she cried, more laughter in the warning than anger, "you're sick!"

He ran his teeth along her toe again, then closed his lips over it, sucking. She gulped hard at the erotic surge that ran through her. Their gazes collided, and now she could detect more in his eyes than mirth. Something warm and thrilling. As thrilling as the stimulating, teasing touch of his mouth. *And his tongue*! She would never have believed that such bizarre contact with Jack's lips could make her feel so—so pleasant. And it wasn't the sort of pleasant feeling she would expect between two old friends, either.

Flustered, her body went all flushed and shaky. Jack was a friend. A dear friend. The word "love" wasn't even in her vocabulary. Her heartbeat accelerated, her breathing grew erratic and her throat went dry. She didn't want to dwell on the clashing emotions roiling around inside her, didn't want to put form and meaning to them.

Shoving the indistinct fancy to a back shelf in her brain, she managed to wriggle out of his grasp. Springing up to sit, she pulled her feet safely beneath her. "Jack Gallagher, I suggest that you consider therapy," she cried, her voice breathless and husky at the same time.

He leaned back against the headboard, his expression satisfied. "I'm that good, huh?"

She crossed her arms in a huff, but the twinkle in his eyes short-circuited her exasperation. After a second, they were both grinning at each other.

"I didn't mean that you should be a foot-sucking therapist," she corrected, unable to keep laughter out of her voice. "I think you need to see somebody about your *problem.*"

His grin grew sly. "Did you really think it was bad?"

She experienced a shiver at the memory of how pleasurable his tongue felt against that most unlikely scrap of anatomy, then forced her lips into puckered thoughtfulness. After a count of ten, she relented. "Okay, so I need therapy, too." With a disdainful sniff, she turned away. "We're both perverts."

He reached down and scooped up her shoes, tossing them onto the bed. "Here, put these on before I do something rash."

She turned back. "Rasher than sucking my toes?" She made a face. "I shudder to think!"

He laughed. "You know what Shakespeare says about that, don't you?"

She frowned at him as she put on her socks. "Do *you*?"

He slid his legs off the bed and slipped into his shoes. When he straightened to tower above her, the sight was so alarmingly enjoyable the air fisted in her lungs. "Tinsley isn't the only person who can quote Shakespeare."

She eyed him askance. "Okay. I'll bite. What did Shakespeare say about toe sucking?"

"The ol' bard said, 'Let us perverts go do lunch.'"

She stared, stunned by the invitation. "You mean it?"

He shrugged casually. "I'm starved. No offense, but one of your toes does not a luncheon make."

She laughed. "Another quote from the ol' bard?"

"Shakespeare didn't say everything." He feigned a hurt look. "Shake a leg, Luce. I need food."

It was strange how her fatigue suddenly disappeared. Scrambling for her shoes, she pulled them on. "I passed the cutest café on the way back." Hopping off the bed, she grabbed his arm. "You know, for a pervert, you can be fun."

When he smiled down at her, a new spring of happiness filled her heart.

"You'd be surprised how often I hear that," he kidded.

It was a shame how happiness could bubble up and then just as quickly evaporate. Thoughts of Desiree leaped into her brain. No doubt the sexy French siren knew all about Jack's lusty perversions.

Lucy bit her lip, but the pain she inflicted on herself didn't outstrip the pang of jealousy she felt in her gut. She flinched. *Jealousy*?

She must have audibly groaned, for at the door, Jack stopped, pulling her to a halt. "Are you okay?"

She couldn't meet his gaze and merely nodded.

Jealousy? Were her feelings for Jack changing? Did she see him as something besides a good friend? Possibly more?

"You sure you feel okay?" he asked, sounding worried. "You've gone pale."

She forced herself to look at him, reaffirming her lie by shaking her head. He bent lower to get a better look into her eyes. A swath of brown hair fell across his brow, reminding her of his wilder teenage days when she'd had a raging little-girl crush on him.

"Lucy?" he coaxed.

"Uh—oh—just hungry, I guess," she muttered, coming out of the trance. She didn't want to think about exactly what—or *who*—she might be hungry for. How stupid could she be? She didn't want to feel an attachment for any man. She wasn't even sure how she felt about Stadler, so how could she be entertaining possessive thoughts about Jack?

He's only doing you a favor, Lucy, her mind screamed, *—as a friend*.

CHAPTER NINE

LUCY sat down on a bench in the shade of a Victorian gazebo. She watched Jack take a drink from the shaded water fountain, fed by one of the natural springs that gave the town its name. Leaning back on her hands, she lazily scanned him. The flat stone was cool against her palms, but the afternoon had been pleasantly warm, and so had Jack's company. She grinned as he straightened, thinking he looked cute in the Panama hat he'd bought in the shop that stocked all manner of headgear.

Feeling in a particularly silly mood, she'd bought a mauve pith helmet, sporting a purple ribbon that tied under her chin.

Jack sat down beside her, adjusting his straw hat farther back on his head. "What next?" he asked.

She sagged against his shoulder. "I'm pooped, but I have to get to that store that caters to cat lovers. I want to get Helen something." She nudged her shopping bag with her foot. "Elissa's going to love that cloisonné frog we got her."

"You think so?" Jack asked with a grin. "I never thought of Elissa as a frog sort of person."

Lucy tipped back her helmet so that she could better see him. "Really?" She was curious about his opinion. "How do you think of Elissa?"

He looked away, focusing on the high stone wall that ran along behind the gazebo, giving the place a cavelike feel. "I think of Elissa as fire." His gaze settled on Lucy's face. "Helen is earth. The little earth mother who loves and nurtures all living things."

Lucy was charmed by his assessment of her sisters.

His smile faded, and she wondered why. Then she thought of something and teased, "If I'm wind, that makes us a seventies rock group. Not very original, Jack."

His grin returned, and he shook his head. "You're not wind, Lucy." He scanned her face, his expression softening. "Air, maybe."

"Air?" She frowned in thought. Air was so—so invisible. Taken for granted. And pretty polluted in most places. "Gee, thanks."

He chuckled. "You're welcome." He flicked her helmet down over her eyes. "And what do you think of when you think of me?"

She resettled her hat so that she could eye him peevishly. "You've heard of the Four Horsemen of the Apocalypse?"

He nodded, his eyes sparkling. "Sure. Moe, Curly, Larry and Pestilence."

She couldn't help herself and grinned, standing up. "Guess which one you are." Grabbing her shopping bag, she started down the pavement path into the welcome, late-afternoon sunshine. The park was coming to life. Redbuds were blossoming over plantings of yellow crocus, pink tulips and sprinklings of blue, purple and white wildflowers, bright bits of color on the hilly, greening landscape.

Eureka Springs was like a Victorian theme park, with block after block of picturesque stone walls and terraces that housed an Easter-basket array of colorful homes and quaint inns. Lucy thought that any of the turn-of-the-century residences in town could have substituted for the famous Victorian home in the movie *Psycho*—only a warm, fuzzy, Disney version of the film. She secretly hoped each and every one of the old houses had its own ghost lounging around in its pink or yellow or baby blue attic. She'd heard rumors that some did.

She could turn her head almost anywhere in town and civilization disappeared. On the other side of the street, you might be treated to breathtaking woods or treacherous drop-offs. Lucy pictured heartbroken lovers leaping from the plentiful limestone bluffs into the dense wooded valleys below.

And greenery was everywhere—trees, bushes, shrubs, vines. Lucy almost felt that if she was inattentive, she would be swallowed up by it all and burped up somewhere as a rosebush. But apparently, that hardly ever happened, for small animals scampered fearlessly underfoot, peeked from behind trees or scurried into half-hidden caves. And the sky was filled with the bright hue of birds flitting unafraid amid the teeming foliage.

Of course, the famous springs abounded around town, seeping from massive stone outcroppings or harnessed in drinking fountains in charming little parks. The clean, clear water was welcome and cool after a long day of tromping over uneven cobbled streets or up and down incalculable steps.

"Where are we going now?" Jack asked, catching up and taking her bag from her.

"The cat store."

"Oh, right. Helen."

"Earth mother," she said, surprised at the rancor in her voice. Why was she jealous that Jack thought so fondly of Helen—and that he thought of Elissa as fire? Why couldn't he think of *her* as earth or fire? Air. Phooey. Nothingness!

"How many pets does she have now?" he asked, breaking through her mental griping.

His fingers encircled her elbow, forcing her to slow her pace. She hadn't realized she'd practically been running. From what, she had no idea.

"Uh—Helen?" She shook herself, trying to get back on track. "Oh, her cats. Yes. She still has Thalia, of course, and Love. And Cracker. You remember her three-legged dog?''

''Right.''

''Helen said she's adopted a crippled cat named Mousie. Seems the little dear was hurt in a fall and one of her forepaws is paralyzed. Gets around fine, though, just slides the bad paw along the floor. And there's Beaver and Pandora and, uh, one more. Miss Fluffy, I think.''

''Any more dogs?'' Jack asked, amusement in his voice.

''One. A female. Can't recall the name, but apparently Cracker brought her home. So I guess she's really Cracker's dog.''

Jack laughed. ''Great. Now her pets are bringing home pets.''

Lucy smiled. ''Luckily, their house sitter used to work for a vet, so he's accustomed to caring for lots of animals.''

''I have a feeling there'll be more before she's through, if I know my Helen.''

Lucy swallowed hard. *My Helen.* She supposed Helen was Jack's favorite. Her little sister was quiet, sweet and about the most kindhearted person in the world. Why wouldn't Jack love her the most? ''Well, their house in upstate New York has ten acres around it.'' She forced herself to sound cheerful. ''They could have a zoo if they chose to.''

For some reason, she didn't feel conversational anymore and she couldn't imagine why. They'd had a great afternoon. Jack had even bought one of those instant cameras and they'd taken lots of silly pictures—

''What about another picture?'' Jack's suggestion startled her. Could he read her mind? He indicated the direction. ''Let's go over there beside the tree.''

A huge oak sat amid a landscaped area that would

certainly hold a myriad of flowers later in the year. A low branch forked off from the main trunk about three feet up and nearly parallel to the ground. Jack led Lucy to the tree and put down her sack of souvenirs.

Spanning her waist with his hands, he hoisted her up to the branch. He surprised her by sprinting back to the path and stopping a stout, middle-aged man who had been walking with a tall, thin woman. "Mind taking a picture of us?" he asked. "We're on our honeymoon." He grinned and thanks to his effervescent charm the couple smiled obligingly. After the man took the camera, Jack showed him the simple mechanism, then ran back to stand beside Lucy. He laid an arm around the branch, brushing her hips as he did.

"You'd better take off those hats," the man suggested. "Your faces aren't going to show."

"And you really must kiss her," the woman added, giggling. "We won't look."

Jack peered at Lucy. "What do you think?" He leaned closer, tugging the ribbon loose at her chin and slipping off her pith helmet. "It would look convincing for you-know-who." He dropped the helmet onto her sack, then flicked off his straw. It sailed to the ground near the man with their camera.

Lucy felt a twinge, but didn't know if it was caused by the reminder of Stadler or the idea of kissing Jack. Now that she'd had thoughts about him that didn't fit into the "best friends" slot, she wasn't sure what she should do. Not caring to analyze her thinking too closely, she merely nodded. After all, a debate about kissing Jack out here in public wasn't worth the embarrassment it would cause. Jack had already said they were on their honeymoon. *Besides*, her mind whispered coyly, *kissing Jack again has been on your mind. Admit it*! "Okay," she murmured, her gaze cast down as she fussed with the top button of her blouse.

When she chanced a peek at his face, his smile came slowly, stretching her nerves tighter. He turned to nod toward the couple. "Great idea." As luck would have it, the branch had positioned her eye-to-eye with him. His face was near, growing nearer, his lips inviting as his mouth shaped itself for kissing.

Heat rushed to her cheeks, and she grew giddy with anticipation. Jack was actually going to…

As his lips met hers, his arm around her hips pressed close, pulling her into him. His free hand moved to the nape of her neck, locking her mouth with his. A beautiful imprisonment. His kiss explored tenderly, sending shivers of desire through her and throwing her stomach into a turbulent spin.

There was soft persuasion in the touch of his mouth, and in a gentle, wordless bribe he somehow managed to cajole her lips to part—moving her to accept the stimulating gifts his tongue could offer.

With the intimate invasion, she experienced a heady, almost delirious gratification. Her arms came up on their own, curling about his shoulders, and she found herself joining the sensual dance of tongues, startled at the depth of her craving. Never had she kissed Stadler with such helpless need. Never had she quivered at his touch this way—so deep down in her core that a restlessness blossomed, making her feel more and more need rather than a quenching of it.

Without warning, he lifted his mouth from hers, backing a step away. She blinked, swayed, and he steadied her. It was only then that she realized there was a tittering of laughter nearby. She turned, feeling drugged, only half-registering that they'd drawn a crowd. The man who'd taken the picture was standing nearby. He handed Jack the camera. "Makes me wish I were twenty years younger." He patted Jack's shoulder. "Takes me back.

Yes, it sure does.'' He turned to his wife and smiled at her. "Let's go back to the hotel, Margaret May.''

His wife's faded gray eyes went wide and her lined cheeks grew ruddy in a blush. It was clear from her husband's tone that Jack and Lucy's kiss had reminded him of the reason he'd married his wife years ago. He walked back to the path and took her hand, tugging her along. The woman looked back and waved. It almost seemed as though there was a thank-you in her eyes.

While their audience dispersed, Jack lifted his hands to Lucy's waist. "I'll help you down.''

Without making eye contact, she nodded. Her throat was too scratchy to speak. As he settled her to the ground, she exhaled through puffed cheeks, wondering if Desiree was this wobbly after one of Jack's kisses. She busied herself straightening her trousers, keeping her face averted, for she knew she was red with shame. How could she have let herself go that way?

"I'm sorry about that, Luce,'' he murmured.

She plucked at a bit of bark that had stuck to her. "About what?'' She cleared the quaking from her voice.

"The kiss. I'm afraid I got carried away—for the picture.''

She swallowed several times. "No problem. I didn't feel a tongue—*a thing*!'' She closed her eyes, wishing she were dead. Her only hope was that he hadn't heard her slip.

"That's good,'' he said, and Lucy had a dreadful feeling there was a touch of amusement in his words.

She started to take a step away to put distance between them, but found her legs too watery. She grabbed for the tree and leaned against it.

"What's the matter?''

"Crick in my knee,'' she lied.

He picked up the sack, depositing her hat inside. "Do you still want to get that gift for Helen?''

"Sure." She inhaled for strength. Pushing away from the tree, she tested her legs. They were steadier, thank heaven. "Let's go."

Taking her arm, he led her toward the path where he plucked up his hat. When he set it on her head, she glanced his way. " Looks better on you." His crooked grin was so breathtaking she dropped her gaze in self-defense. "How's the knee?" he asked.

Better than my lips, she wanted to shout. They throbbed with every beat of her heart and felt as swollen as weather balloons.

Stupid lips.

Lucy was lonesome and alone a lot during the next two days. So she spent her "honeymoon" browsing in the little art galleries along the narrow downtown streets of Eureka Springs, which were devoid of stop signals and other signs of the twentieth century.

She couldn't recount the number of times she rode the trolley or loitered in city parks where impromptu jazz and blues concerts abounded. Wistfully, she gazed after other honeymooning couples walking arm in arm, oblivious to anything but their love for each other. To her dismay, during all this lonely time, her thoughts turned invariably toward Jack.

Jack.

As quickly as she batted down romantic notions, they crowded back, implanting vivid pictures of the two of them together, arms entwined, with eyes for no one but each other. The foolish scenario was getting monotonous, considering the fact that Desiree didn't seem to have anything else to do but make long, hot calls to Jack—day and night. Night and day. No wonder he had so much trouble getting any work done.

Every time the phone rang, Lucy's stomach knotted. Which was crazy. And even as she pretended nonchalance, leaving Jack to his privacy, she was getting more and more upset and confused. What was going on with her emotions lately? Did she care for Stadler or did she loathe him? Did she want Jack for a friend or—or…?

She hadn't spent much time with her pretend husband in the past forty-eight hours, which left her feeling depressed. Business concerns were uppermost on his agenda. Plus the property deal in Branson was coming to a boil, with negotiations, renegotiations and re-renegotiations.

In truth, when she came back to the room after several hours of sight-seeing, she enjoyed sitting on the bed beside him as he talked with business associates on the phone. While he could be funny and charming, he was always logical. He spoke with authority, yet was never unkind or argumentative. She admired that ability. She'd never been good at confronting a problem and explaining analytically why it should go her way. Usually she got tongue-tied and backed off, hating herself for being such a weenie. Jack never backed off and he never lost.

He seemed to be able to win a fight and never even fight. And he didn't wheedle or manipulate the way Stadler did. Or go behind a person's back. She liked that straightforwardness about Jack. He could be trusted to be honest and loyal to his friends and candid and fair with his competitors.

That night, they turned in early. Jack had a 6:00 a.m. conference call, and Lucy was just plain tired from all her walking. Rain began to tap against the windows around ten. A short time later, a spring storm swept in. Lightning shot silver flashes through the room, and thunder rattled the patio doors like an angry landlord.

Lucy had long ago outgrown her fear of such atmospheric upheavals, but that didn't mean she'd learned to sleep through them. Besides, tonight she had other upheavals on her mind. The cause of one was not far away, his back to her, apparently peacefully sleeping.

That wasn't fair. How could he sleep so soundly with all this racket going on? She loudly cleared her throat, but the attempt to wake him was covered by a whip crack of thunder. She frowned at herself. How did she think one little throat clearing would bring him awake if he could sleep through this clamor? It was like trying to get someone to taste one shred of parsley in a dish riddled with garlic. Impossible.

Well, Lucy, if you really want his attention, you're going to have to be bold! she told herself. *Touch him*!

She reached out, but saw her hand go death white in another flash of lightning. The starkness of the vision, of her hand halfway to his broad back, stilled her. What was she doing? What did she need to discuss with Jack that was so urgent she planned to wake him from what had to be a sound sleep? She had no answer; she only knew she *needed* to talk to him. Now.

Again, she moved her hand toward him, finally testing the warm hardness of his shoulder with one finger. She pressed, but couldn't move him at all. She sucked in a nervous breath as thunder growled a hair-raising warning. Emboldened by her first tentative effort, she ignored the heavenly omen. It was only weather, not the dictates of some avenging god of sound sleepers.

This time, she palmed his shoulder and shook. He moved with her efforts, but only slightly.

Silence.

She exhaled, dejected. Did the man go into a coma at night? She touched him again, bent on shoving him off the bed if she had to.

"I'm awake, Luce," he murmured, his voice guarded.

At first, she wasn't sure she'd heard him respond, the quiet comment coming on the heels of another snarl of thunder. But when she became aware that the sound was actually human, she instinctively jerked her hand away. *Now what*? She chewed the inside of her cheek, unsure of what to say.

He shifted to his back to face her. His features were indistinct in the darkness. She wished for a lightning strike so that she could see if he was perturbed to be awakened. Quickly she took back the wish. She didn't need extra stress.

"Luce?" he coaxed. "It's not the storm, is it? You're not frightened?"

She smiled, half out of nervousness, half out of thankfulness. There was no temper in his voice. Lightning flashed, and his features appeared for the smallest part of a second, leaving the impression of strong planes, unsmiling masculine lips and deep set, heavily lashed eyes. Wary eyes, not the least drowsy from sleep. She wondered if he had been lying there awake, too.

For some reason, that knowledge gave her strength to speak. "Jack?" she asked, almost too softly to hear.

"Yes?"

"Do you think my hips are too big?"

A crash of thunder filled the air with sound, so Lucy didn't know if he'd answered with a definite yes or no. Or if he'd responded at all. She also wasn't sure why she'd asked such an asinine question—especially in the middle of the night.

"Is this a trick question?" he finally said, and Lucy had a feeling a vague smile rode his lips.

"Tell me the truth, Jack," she said. "I need to know."

"What brought this up—now?"

Apprehension twisting her insides, she turned to better face him. "A couple of days ago, you implied I needed to spend more time on the stair-stepper machine, and I just thought, maybe…"

There was another long pause while Lucy's chest

ached from holding her breath. After a dizzying eternity, she heard a chuckle. "Luce, I was just kidding you. What I said had nothing to do with what I think about your hips."

"But—but do you think they're too big?" She didn't know why she was forcing the issue. "You made the remark, so it must have been floating around in your subconscious."

"Lucy." He reached out, touching her hand, then seeming to think better of it, he drew away. "I think your hips are perfect—ly adequate."

He cleared his throat, and she felt a twinge of suspicion that he wasn't being totally truthful with her. Groaning, she turned away. "Oh, never mind. I know I'm shaped like a pear. It's not your fault."

"Lucy, why do you care what I think?"

She squeezed her eyes tight. He was getting too close to her "upheaval" area. She shook her head, deciding a half-truth was the best option. "I care about your opinion. That's all."

Thunder came crashing down on them like the felling of a huge tree, and Lucy was grateful for the barrier of sound. She needed barriers right now. Any kind. A bundling board would be good. Her emotions were messing with her mind, and she didn't know what to do—or what she might do.

"I certainly don't have the hips of a high-fashion model," she blurted, then bit her tongue. *Where had that come from*?

"I suppose you don't," he replied, sounding careful. But instead of being upset, she felt drawn to him for his truthfulness. "Honestly, Luce—"

The phone jangled in the darkness, making Lucy jump. She knew instinctively who was calling and she vaulted to her knees. "Doesn't that woman have anything *else* to do?'' she cried, astounded by the depth of irritation she felt.

Jack was reaching for the phone when she spoke. He lifted the receiver, but put a hand over it so the person on the other end couldn't hear. ''Why, Luce,'' he said with soft reproach, ''what's come over you?''

She allowed her head to loll back so that she could eye the ceiling. ''Do you want me to go into the bathroom so you can be alone?'' she whispered. ''I can take a book.''

''Good idea.'' Removing his hand from the receiver, he spoke into it. That smoky, sexy growl he reserved for his haute couture lover made the hackles on her neck rise. Lord, how she was starting to hate it when he talked like that. Whispering words of love in a language she didn't understand. *And…*her brain insisted on adding, *to a woman who isn't you.*

As Lucy slid from the bed, she gritted her teeth, driving that wayward thought from her mind. It was of no interest to her if Jack thought Desiree's bony backside was without rival in the entire cosmos.

In a melancholy mood, Lucy strolled in the hotel garden, trying to enjoy the clear night. A thousand stars were out and the moon was new. Everything smelled fresh and clean. A perfect night for lovers. She cringed at her turn of mind.

All that day she had been unaccountably depressed. Jack had clearly sensed her gloom because after long hours in the hotel room dealing with his business concerns, he'd insisted on taking her out to dinner. They dressed up and went to a local restaurant noted for its rack of lamb. Lucy had never eaten the dish before and feared that if she ever did again, she would recall this evening with Jack too fondly for her own good.

The experience seemed so much like a date, she kept

getting her mind screwed up on the subject. He was her date. He was her friend. He was her date. He was her friend. For some reason, the two didn't go together to her liking. At the end of the evening she'd wanted badly to be kissed good-night.

Ironically, Jack didn't kiss her or leave her at her door, but came in with her, stating he had more work to do. He'd be downstairs in the hotel office sending some faxes, but first he'd take a shower.

So she'd left him to his privacy and wandered aimlessly along the winding limestone paths, examining the awakening garden. Most flowers were not showing themselves yet. Even so, the place was quiet and pleasant. She supposed it was lucky for her that the other guests at the hotel were real honeymooners who had better things to do with their nights than drift alone in gardens. So she had the place to herself.

She was gradually drawn to the central fountain. Four gracefully jumping fish formed the center tower. From their open mouths, cascades of water poured into an upper tier. From there, the water coursed over the scalloped side, a never-ending waterfall, into the lower reservoir, where colorful fish darted and flashed. The outer rim of the structure was fashioned from wide stone slabs into a curved seating area.

Lucy sat down and watched the play of water, trying to calm herself with the tranquillity of the tinkling sound. Nature's music. Usually the sound of a fountain was calming and restful, but tonight, her nerves were so raw, her emotions so tattered, she didn't think she would ever find the peace to enjoy simple pleasures again—not of a songbird or a breeze rustling a treetop, or even a thrill at a baby's first smile. Her emotions were broken, charred, stomped into dust.

Stadler had wounded her deeply. She'd put her heart and soul into their relationship—their *long-distance* relationship—for two endless years. She'd looked at no other man, thought of no other man.

Then he had ripped her heart from her, trampled it, made her think she could never believe in love again. And here it was, only three weeks later, and she was looking at Jack in a way she'd never thought possible. Her heart doubled its beat when he came into a room, and she felt as though heaven smiled down on her every time he took her hand to help her across a street.

What was wrong with her? How fickle could she be? And how could she let herself fall for a man who was so obviously in love with someone else?

Was she bent on self-destruction? Did she need professional help?

Trailing a finger in the water, she closed her eyes, not wanting to think at all.

Restless, she jumped up, looking at her watch. It had been nearly forty-five minutes since Jack left her. He would be in the hotel office by now—doing his faxing or whatever. She might as well take her shower and be in bed before he got back. It would be best not to be awake. Unconsciousness, she'd discovered, was her best defense against having thoughts she shouldn't be having. Thoughts that would get her nowhere.

Listlessly, she climbed up the steps to their room and moved almost in a trance to the armoire to get her T-shirt and panties. On the way to the bathroom, she stopped. She could hear the shower running.

The door stood ajar. She frowned thoughtfully, then shook her head. Jack was such a pulled-together man. Why was it that he had a hard time remembering to turn off a shower? She smiled to herself. It was kind of cute—to discover he had such an odd kink in his character. Kicking off her heels, she found herself wondering if Desiree ever had to take a cold shower after one of Jack's forgetful moments.

She opened the bathroom door, deciding a cold shower might just suit her. Erotic thoughts about Jack were coming too hot and heavy lately, and she needed to cool off in more ways than one.

She laid her T-shirt and panties across the rim of the old-fashioned tub. Then she slipped out of her dress and hung it on the hook behind the door. After removing her underclothes, she grabbed the shower door handle and stepped inside—right into a very solid male object.

"*Jack*!" she cried as something thudded to the tiles. Her mind caught onto the fact that it had been a bar of soap. She'd either knocked it from his hand as she stumbled into him, or he'd dropped it in his shock.

She lurched back, but her foot landed squarely on the soap, making her slide. She flailed, trying not to fall, and found herself hanging helplessly from Jack's solid neck.

His arms came around her to steady her. She blinked as the warm spray dampened the side of her face and body.

"My God," Jack whispered hoarsely. "Luce?"

"I—I thought you were going to fax—"

"I decided to do that first. I…" He stopped, swallowed, seeming to be at a loss.

She hung on, but suddenly she no longer felt any fear of falling. Not even any embarrassment. She clung to him with a pure, wild need to be near him, body to body. She stared up into cinnamon eyes, long lashes, spangled and sparkling, watching his expression, a mixture of shock and desire. That split second in his arms, looking into his wonderful eyes, held her awakening, and she faced the truth at last.

She loved Jack Gallagher. She always had. But all those years ago, she'd been a peacemaking little girl and he'd been a handsome teenage rebel. He'd come from a different world, and she'd known in her heart that he was destined for greatness. He'd had such strength, such

drive, but it had been mixed with an anger that frightened her.

The anger was gone now; just the drive remained. He
was no longer a rebel, but a mover and shaker. He was
still wildly handsome, though, with eyes that beckoned
without words. He had been so different from her, so
much older, but even so, she'd loved him. Loved him
from the first moment. And when he'd run away, she'd
put that love aside, trying to convince herself it had been
a childhood crush.

Now she could see that Stadler had been nothing more
than an ill-defined replica of Jack. *Oh, how blind she'd
been*.

Jack was staring at her. He seemed to be waiting for
something as he gently held her. She could feel his
arousal, and it made her bold. She moved against him,
her breasts relishing the rough, slick feel of his chest.
"You're soapy," she breathed, her heart pounding so
loudly she could hardly hear herself talk.

He half smiled. "I'm taking a shower."

She smiled, too, feeling like a siren, a temptress, for
the first time in her life. It felt good. "What a coincidence," she murmured.

His smile faded, and his eyes took on an odd luster.
"Lucy?" he asked a little raggedly. "What are we doing?"

She toyed with his soapy chest hair, stroking, pulling
it into frothy tufts. "I'm not sure," she admitted. Her
smile faded, too. "What do you want to do?" Her gaze
lifted to meet his again, this time shyly.

He opened his lips to speak, then stopped. He clamped
his jaw shut, and she watched a muscle tense in his
cheek. Visions of Desiree leaped into her mind. It was
so clear he was trying to remain loyal to the woman he
loved. He was aroused, but that was the nature of the
male animal. Female nudity was a turn-on. Especially
when that female was plastered up against him. Rubbing,

teasing. The poor dear couldn't help himself, but he was fighting it.

Drat that Desiree! Why did she have to exist? Lucy felt a surge of anger. She wouldn't let that *person* stop her. She loved Jack, too. She'd loved him years and years longer. A biting sweetness overpowered her as she got used to the words, and she felt a dawning need to know Jack completely, a need as strong as the necessity of taking air into her lungs. *She loved him*! Her body trembled with it. Slipping her hands back up to encircle his neck, she pressed her breasts into his chest, thrust her body against his arousal. This time, she used no coquetry, but gazed at him with candor. "Jack, make love to me."

He sucked in a breath that seemed shuddery, his hands spreading along her back, drawing her closer. She could feel the heavy beat of his heart and prayed that the tumult in his chest was not mere lust, but an emotion much more dear.

"Oh, Lucy…" He groaned, then lowered his head and kissed her shoulder. His lips moved deliciously along her collarbone to her neck. "I want you.…" His kisses tantalized and enlivened her jaw before he drew his lips away to gaze at her face. "But I have to ask you a question."

She shivered with the desire for him to sweep her into his arms, to take her to a lover's paradise. The woman in her sensed that he could show her pleasures she had never experienced, never expected to know. Her body quivered for the release she knew she could find only in his arms. "What?" she asked breathlessly. "Ask me. But hurry." She didn't know what the question was, didn't care. She just wanted it to be over so that he would love her.

His eyes were dark with emotion, and she was stunned to detect a measure of pain there, too. "Lucy, before we do something we can't undo, ask yourself honestly, would you feel good about it in the morning?''

His voice broke. She'd never known Jack's voice to break. Plainly, this was difficult for him. She was forced to think about Desiree again. About Jack's situation. He was here as a friend of the family, and now she was trying to seduce him. How unfair could she be? What kind of selfish beast had she become, trying to come between Jack and the woman he loved? She hated that kind of greedy, self-centered creature. Did she plan to become one herself?

She looked up into his marvelous eyes and watched him watch her. She could tell the decision was hers. She had been the one to blunder into his shower—to tease and taunt him with her body.

Her fingers ached to touch him all over. Her lips ached to kiss him, to know again the hot, sexy message of his lips, his tongue. But what would one mindless night of passion do to their friendship? He was right. It could never be undone. She was suddenly frightened. Would Jack avoid her, be embarrassed for her, for them? She couldn't stand that. To see pity in his eyes. Or worse, *regret*, for being disloyal to Desiree.

A despondent shiver rushed through her as she began to lower her arms from his broad shoulders. Against her will, her hands lingered, relishing the feel of him beneath her palms. Her heart registered every scent, every texture, with reverence, and she knew the memory of this moment would never fade away.

With the most reluctance she had ever felt in her life, she backed away from him, and with trembling hands, she covered herself. Her whole body blazed with humiliation. ''Thank you for having the strength of character to show me how shamefully I was behaving,'' she whispered brokenly. Spinning away, she cried, ''The honeymoon's over, Jack. Let's go home.''

CHAPTER TEN

THE drive back to Branson was silent, the tension between Lucy and Jack ricocheting around inside his car like bullets. He peered at her from time to time, hating what he saw. She was huddled as far from him as she could get, her face turned away in pretended fascination with the scenery. Since it was midnight and clouds had pushed across the sky, obliterating even the stars, the forested hills that zoomed by were a shadowy blur. Her remote posture was obviously more to avoid his company than any interest in her surroundings.

Jack knew she didn't want to face him. She thought she'd humiliated herself. He gripped the leather steering wheel as though he wanted to strangle it. When she'd crashed into him in the shower earlier that night, he'd been so stunned he hadn't known what to do. It was painfully clear that he'd done everything wrong. Big stud, Jack Gallagher—his brain had turned to mud. He'd wanted her so badly—wanted her to tell him she loved him. But when she backed away, obviously regretting her wantonness…

Jack stifled a groan as another surge of lust twisted his gut. *Dammit to hell*! He'd had women chasing him all his life—climbing in through his bedroom windows, even stalking him. Why did the one woman in the world who could resist his charms be the one woman in the world he loved? What had he done that was so bad that he had to be punished this cruelly?

Trying to concentrate on his driving, Jack maneuvered around a hairpin turn along the narrow road that undulated through the Ozark Mountains. At night, the route

was treacherous, not well lit. And his mind was precar-
iously divided. He wanted to pull to the side of the road,
take her into his arms and tell her not to be upset. That
he loved her, and he was so, so sorry for anything he'd
done to cause her pain.

It was clear now that Stadler had more of a hold on
Lucy's heart than she realized. And worse, Jack had less.
Damn! Why had he insisted she think about the morning? Why hadn't he simply grabbed the paradise she
offered and then tried to survive with that one glorious
memory for the rest of his life? Why had his damnable
pride insisted that she admit she loved him—loved him
the way he loved her? With all her soul.

He cast her another pensive glance. "Lucy?" She
jumped at the sound, but didn't turn, so he went on solemnly, "Don't do this to yourself—"

"Let's not talk about it," she broke in, sounding desolate but adamant. "If you care at all about me, Jack,
you'll never mention it again." The last word came out
in a sob.

He gritted his teeth on a curse.

The rest of the drive home was made in stony silence.

Lucy used her key when they arrived, since it was nearly
one o'clock in the morning. Neither of them wanted to
disturb Elissa—or answer any question about their sudden return.

They went downstairs, neither speaking. Lucy was
bent on escaping to her room. Jack sensed it, but he
couldn't let her go like that. "Luce?" That one, whispered word stilled her at her door. "Wait a second."

He watched her shoulders rise and knew she was gathering the courage to turn around. When she did, he
tossed his suitcase on the couch and flicked the latches.
Opening it, he pulled out a brown plastic sack and

straightened. He started to speak, but faced with the bleakness in her blue eyes, he was struck dumb.

His urge to take her into his arms swelled powerfully, and he moved toward her, but the step she took away from him was like having a bucket of ice water heaved in his face. He stopped a few paces away, not wanting her to feel threatened. With his bungling, he'd done enough emotional damage to her for one night. Holding out the package, he said, "I bought this for you."

She shifted her sad gaze from his face to the package, then back. She didn't speak.

He managed a melancholy half smile. "I noticed you didn't buy yourself anything but that nutty hat. So I thought…"

She didn't respond, merely stared at him, her dispirited gaze touching his with reluctance.

A surge of irritation raced through him. "*Dammit*, Lucy." His tone was sharper than he'd meant it to be, and he could see its effect as tears formed in her eyes. She must be thinking he was ashamed of her weakness. Which wasn't true at all. "You didn't do anything wrong," he offered more gently.

"Don't be kind to me, Jack," she warned, her lips thinning.

"I'm not being kind," he shot back, wishing with all that was left of his heart that she would stop looking at him that way. "I haven't been kind about anything—"

"*Don't!*" She held up a warning hand. "I asked you! *Please*."

He clamped his jaws, hating the finality in her gaze. Furious with himself for a dream gone terribly awry, he ripped the plastic bag away, presenting her with a doll made from corn husks. An angel. He'd seen it and thought of her, with its bright, corn-silk hair and halo of braided golden ribbons. Such a delicate, pale figure, unpretentiously lovely, with dainty hands holding a golden star, the faceless head slightly bowed. Fragile corn-husk wings, like big loops on a bow, hovered airily at her back.

"I saw her and I thought of you," he murmured, knowing every word out of his mouth sounded lame, unworthy.

She looked at the offering, and a tear slid down her cheek. Reaching out, she took it from him, then traced along its fine hair with one finger. She didn't smile. Seconds ticked by, long, miserable seconds, as Jack watched another tear skim down her face to tremble on her chin. Finally, she met his gaze, startling him by thrusting the gift in his direction. "I'm not a little girl anymore, Jack. I don't want…" He made it clear he wouldn't take it back by shrugging his hands into his pockets. She swallowed hard. As another tear slid down her face, she dropped the angel at his feet and spun away.

The door clicked shut between them, and though the sound was almost nonexistent, in his heart it felt like a nuclear blast. For a long time, he stood there, just staring, as his world crumbled. The woman he loved could no longer even accept inexpensive tokens from him. She was repelled by the idea that she'd wanted him—even momentarily.

And she was his wife.

He had a feeling that after tonight she wouldn't want to go through with the pretense. Or what she thought was a pretense.

What was he going to do? A savage grief overwhelmed him. How could he love her so desperately, and she not even…?

He glared at the angel doll, laying facedown on the rag rug. Bile rose in his throat and pain tore at his heart. Unable to help himself, he bent to scoop it up, then turned away. Guilt pressed down on him from above and squeezed him from all sides until he could hardly breathe. He couldn't believe what he'd done. All his strategies and deceit had *injured* Lucy, far from accomplishing what he'd hoped for. He was a damned bottom feeder with unmitigated conceit. *How dare he actually marry the woman without her knowledge*! He deserved Lucy's contempt, and his body shuddered with that knowledge.

He wanted to punch holes in the walls, yell bloody murder to the high heavens, run upstairs and kick Stadler's pompous, suspicious ass around his room. He wanted to, wanted to…

After gently placing the doll in his suitcase, he sank onto the couch, dropping his face into his hands. He knew what he really wanted to do. He wanted to walk though Lucy's door, take her into his arms and make wild, magic love to her. He wanted to tell her how hopelessly he loved her, and he wanted to hear her scream out her love for him. To wake the whole state of Missouri. That's what he wanted. In a perfect world, that's what he would have done. And the state of Missouri would be waking up right now.

Unfortunately, the world was far from perfect.

So tonight—for the first time in his life—Jack Gallagher cried.

Lucy sat curled on the couch, cuddling little Lucille Gloriana Lord. She tried not to think about Jack as she scanned the adorable face of her namesake. But the task proved impossible. He'd been gone most of the day. She didn't know much about buying and selling property, but she still doubted that finalizing the land deal for Jack's newest restaurant could be taking all this time.

Little Glory, as the baby was called, gurgled, taking a firm grip on her aunt's finger. A tentative smile lifted Lucy's lips. But her thoughts immediately tumbled back to Jack. It was happening anyway—what she'd feared. He was ignoring her: He was ashamed for her—so appalled by her failed seduction in the shower that he could hardly stand to be around her. Her heart twisted. She might as well have gone ahead and jumped him bodily, forced the issue. Had sex. At least she would have had that one night to remember, to cling to.

She blinked back tears. Jack was so honorable. Another bout of shame enveloped her, and her whole body flamed.

"Well, Stadler," Elissa said, breaking through Lucy's unhappy ramblings, "why did Sareena leave us? Did she finally get smart?"

Lucy's glance darted to Stadler, who was standing before the hearth, looking professorial in his tweed jacket, a pipe clenched between his teeth. He took it out to better glare at Elissa. "Her daddy's birthday is Sunday, and he couldn't stand the idea of his princess missing his day. I don't blame him." He took a puff on his pipe. "Besides, she wanted to start purchasing her trousseau."

"Trousseau?" Elissa appeared to fight a grin. "You can cut holes in jeans in Branson just as easily as in St. Louis."

"Shut up, Elissa," Stadler said, an angry tic kicking to life in his jaw.

The redhead looked up. "Well, pardon me for expressing an opinion." She lifted the twin she held in her arms so the baby faced Stadler. "Now, Elissa Gillian dear, look at that tweedy man and remember him. When you become president, have him deported."

"Elissa!" Helen shook her head at her sister. "That's not the sort of auntlike advice Damien and I had in mind when we named her after you."

Elissa placed the baby against her shoulder and began to pat gently. "Sorry," she mumbled, but didn't look very repentant.

"I should think you would be," Stadler said, clamping his pipe between his teeth.

Elissa pinned him with a scowl. "Tinsley, if you're going to smoke that thing, go outside. I don't want my little Elissa Gillian's lungs to fill up with tar."

He made an irritated sound. "That cold front came in with a fury. It's freezing outside."

She gave him an impatient look. "There's this new invention. It's called a coat. Now go. This is a no-smoking inn."

Once he was gone, Lucy heaved a sigh so overflowing with unhappiness she drew her sisters' glances.

"What's the matter, honey?" Helen rose from the rug. "Tired of holding Glory?"

Lucy smiled at her younger sister. "Of course not." She cast a surreptitious glance at the parlor entrance. "I just wish *he* would leave!"

"Don't we all," Elissa said morosely.

Lucy shifted to look at the redhead. "Why can't he accept my marriage to Jack at face value and leave me alone?"

"Because he's basically a deceitful snake and assumes everybody else is," Elissa said.

"And is he *wrong*?" Lucy cried. She felt like a snake, too—a lovesick one. She was helplessly in love with Jack, but she couldn't tell him, couldn't embarrass him any more than she already had.

And, of course, there was Desiree.

Silence stretched between the sisters. Lucy knew they were thinking the same thing. They'd behaved no better than Stadler, with the fake engagement and then, worst of all, the counterfeit marriage.

Clearing her throat, Helen stepped up to Lucy. "Glory needs to be changed. I'll take her up to Damien. It's his turn, and I think he's through writing his political column by now." She turned to Elissa. "Can you bring

Gilly in a little while? It's time for her to go to bed, too.''

Elissa kissed the infant's fuzzy head. ''I'll think about it.'' She grinned at Helen. ''And thanks for naming this sweet darling after me.''

Helen laughed, snuggling Glory to her breast. ''After the raving mess you were during our little joke, I'm glad, too.'' Helen giggled, turning away. ''Remember, don't keep Gilly up too long.''

On cue, the baby burped, and Elissa's eyes went wide. ''Oh, oh, I think Madam President just upchucked all over me.''

Lucy tried hard to keep from grinning.

Elissa stood, patting the baby's back. ''Now, young lady, is that any way to treat your mentor, your teacher, your political guru?'' She hurried toward the door. ''Helen, *wait*, your daughter wants you.''

All of a sudden, the parlor was empty and still, but for the crackle of the fire. Lucy's mood plummeted. Once the distraction of babies and sisters was gone, Jack's solemn face loomed in her brain, wreaking havoc.

Wanting to erase the stark vision, she vaulted up and began to pace. He'd told her this morning he was *leaving* on Monday. He had to spend a week in New York, then a couple of weeks in London.

London. She stumbled to a stop before the hearth, planting her hands on the mantel to steady herself. As she stared into the fire, her mind scrambled to places she didn't want to go. There was a tunnel under the English Channel now, and a person could travel so easily to Paris from London.

Jack would see Desiree. He would make love to her. Lucy dug her fingers into the wood, not caring if she broke every single nail into jagged shards. She wouldn't have believed she could hurt more than she already did, but the vision of Jack and his ladylove...

She felt sick and battled down the image. It was Friday now. He'd told her that by the time he got back from London, then spent a few days in Chicago before returning to Branson with his architect, Stadler would be gone. She only had to continue the pretense through the weekend, really. Once he'd left for New York, it would be easier. Then, in a month, when he got back, they could end it.

End it.

She felt ice spread through her veins at the thought. He'd said it quietly, matter-of-factly. Then he'd left. He'd hardly looked at her. Or had it been she who had hardly looked at him? Did it even matter? The important thing was, they'd been so stiff with each other. So uneasy. She fought down a shudder. Oh, why had she been so weak? Why couldn't she have the strength of character Jack had? Why had she made a gigantic fool of herself?

She felt a tug on her arm and was swung into an embrace before she could react. It stunned her to realize that Stadler was kissing her hard on the mouth. His lips were cold, so it was clear he'd just come inside. Wide-eyed, she struggled from his grasp, backing away. "What do you think you're doing?"

He took her hand with his chilled one. In her utter shock, she didn't have the presence of mind to yank away. "'They dream in courtship,'" he murmured, "'but in wedlock wake.'"

"*What*?" she cried, exasperated. "Stadler, I hate it when you quote Shakespeare. What do you want?"

His brow creased and he drank in a sharp breath. "Lucy-pet, I know why you returned from your honeymoon early."

She eyed him with umbrage. "Oh, Stadler. You're completely—"

"You realized your mistake." He took her other hand

and now was holding them both firmly. ''You and I were meant for each other and nothing either of us do will alter that.''

''Stadler, don't—''

''I must speak of it, Lucy-pet,'' he cut in, passion in his voice. ''I realize now that it was a mistake to get engaged to Sareena. I thought her father could help me. She was a sweet, pliable woman, much like you in many ways.'' He stopped, raised one of her hands to his lips and pressed a moist, cool kiss on her knuckles. ''Our long separation made me forget the true rapture of our feelings for one another. I've decided I'm going to send Sareena a letter telling her our engagement is off.''

She swallowed with distaste, the feel of his lips against her skin disgusting. ''Too bad you can't borrow *mine* to copy, but I threw it away,'' she muttered.

His glance lifted to meet hers, his eyes becoming slits. ''Lucy-pet, sarcasm doesn't become you.''

She yanked from his hold, wheeling away. ''Oh, Stadler, this is—''

''I honestly believed that you and Gallagher were trying to deceive me, that the wedding was a fake. But after I checked out that Nate Broom person and discovered he was a *real* minister, I saw red. I suddenly knew the mistake I'd made.'' He grabbed her shoulders, forcing her to face him. ''I want you back, Lucy. Get your marriage annulled and run away with me. Say you will, my love, say yes.'' His voice was high-pitched, pleading.

Lucy blinked. She'd been in such turmoil she had only been half listening. But one statement caught in her battered consciousness and stuck.

''…*discovered he was a* real *minister…*''

''What…what did you say?'' she whispered.

His expression gained hope and he tugged her closer. ''I said, say yes, my love. Tell me you'll run away with me. Leave your husband. You know you only married him for revenge. I forgive you for that. I just want you back.''

''You—you checked on Nate's credentials?'' Her voice was strained, hoarse.

He squeezed her shoulders, looking contrite. ''I wanted to be able to throw the truth in your faces once you returned, but when just this afternoon I received proof that he was the real thing, my life ended.''

She was in shock. Though she tried to speak, no words came.

''Run away with me, Lucy-pet. I promise I'll make you happy.''

She gaped at him, feeling as if a giant fist had caught her by the throat and cut off her oxygen. The Reverend Nate Broom was real? She was *married* to Jack? Why would any man marry a woman and not tell her about it? And what about Desiree? *This couldn't be true*! But Stadler was an intelligent man, not likely to be wrong about something this important.

She was bewildered. ''I—I…Stadler, please, I need time to think.''

Without waiting for his response, she rushed down the stairs to her basement room. After she slammed the door behind her, her thoughts turned to Jack.

Her husband?

Her husband!

''Honorable, trustworthy Jack,'' she muttered, murder blossoming in her heart.

CHAPTER ELEVEN

LATER that evening, Helen, Elissa, Damien, Stadler and a few of the inn's guests congregated before the welcome fire in the parlor. The twins were fast asleep, though Damien carried a baby monitor on his belt just in case.

The conversation was light, breezy and fun. Damien's exciting years as a CNN correspondent held no end of interesting stories, and he was entertaining them with an amusing tale about a certain foreign diplomat and his mistress and how they were found out—on live television.

Everyone laughed uproariously. Even Lucy managed to smile, but her heart wasn't in it. She had fine-tuned every fiber of her being to listen for Jack's return.

At nine o'clock sharp, she heard the sound of his approaching car, of the front door opening, of masculine footsteps entering the parlor. She swallowed. He was here. A soft, husbandly kiss on her cheek told her that Jack was leaning over the back of the sofa. She knew he was doing it for the "pretense" she'd promised to go along with through the weekend.

What pretense! her mind screamed.

Preparing for his return, she'd planned for the past two hours, so she managed to put a hand on his when he rested his palm on her shoulder. And she managed to turn to him with a loving smile. "Hi, darling," she said brightly. "Everything work out?"

He smiled back, but she could see the flicker of surprise in his eyes. "Yes." He straightened, drawing his fingers from her touch. "I got a good deal."

"How marvelous for you, love," she cooed.

His eyes widened a fraction.

She patted the sofa. "Join us? Damien's telling some very funny stories."

He surveyed the room, his grin seemingly easy. "Maybe later. I need a shower. Long day."

"You go shower, lover." She threw him a kiss that he didn't catch, and she wondered why. His smile had dimmed. For a man who'd married her behind her back, he certainly wasn't acting much like a new husband. Anger surging, she added sweetly, "Don't be surprised if I join you."

He blinked, scanned the group again. When he returned his gaze to hers, he nodded. "There's an idea." His grin was rakish and debilitating, but it didn't quite reach his eyes. Even though his message was mixed, she could feel the effects of that smile all the way to her toes. What was running through his *dis*honorable, *un*trustworthy, totally diabolic mind? She was at a loss, but she darn well intended to get to the bottom of it.

"Oh, Jack," Elissa called as he headed out the door. "Jule wanted me to tell you she and Hirk loved the all-expenses-paid weekend in the bridal suite at the Springfield Hilton. She said it was the closest thing they've had to a honeymoon."

He turned, nodded, but his expression was serious. "It was the least I could do." Without further comment, he turned away and was gone.

"Hmm," Elissa pondered aloud. "He doesn't look all that happy."

"He's tired," Helen said, snuggling under Damien's arm. "He's had a lot going on lately."

"I don't think he looks well," Stadler commented.

"You should *ever* look so well," Elissa said with a short laugh. "Now, Damien, go on. Tell us about that Russian prince you interviewed, the one who had that hidden 'sex chamber' in his castle. I'm dying for details.''

As Damien enthralled the rest of the group, Lucy peeked at the mantel clock. Her timing had to be perfect. She'd had two hours to formulate her strategy. At first, she'd been furious, but then she'd realized that a true marriage with Jack was what she wanted. She loved him, but did he love her?

Why else would he marry her? But if he loved her, then why his reluctance to act like a husband? He'd had plenty of chances. He'd slept in her bed. *And the shower fiasco*! She could strangle him for that alone. But most confusing of all—what was going on with Desiree?

The whole situation was so bizarre, she didn't know what to think. She had to hear from Jack's own lips why he'd lied to her and tricked her. And if he loved her, he was darned well going to say so.

And soon.

She felt like a fool. How dare he play the kindly, sacrificing friend when he was her husband all the time? A woman had the right to be coy and reticent, to be pursued by the man she loved—not rejected at every turn. Irritated by his unfathomable game, she had spent the past two hours devising her revenge.

The clock struck nine-fifteen. Time to make her move. She stood abruptly, drawing Damien's gaze. He stopped in the middle of a sentence. ''Leaving us?''

She nodded, faking a smile. ''I forgot to tell Jack something.'' She made a quick exit, hoping her demeanor seemed normal. She breathed a sigh of relief when she heard Damien resume his story.

When she got downstairs, the shower was no longer running, but she could hear Jack in the bathroom. She stood before the door, her heart pounding against her ribs so hard she feared the protective bones would be pulverized. Her body shook with panic, but she knew she had to hit him hard and fast where it hurt. And the time was *now*.

Grabbing the doorknob, she pushed it open and barged inside. Jack was standing at the sink, a towel wrapped around his waist, his chin half-glazed with shaving cream. At her abrupt entry, he dropped his razor. It clattered into the porcelain sink. ''Lucy?''

She made herself look away from him, pretending total disinterest in his marvelous male body. ''Pardon me, Jack.'' She moved briskly to the linen closet and threw open the doors. ''I need to get my suitcase.'' She reached up, but the shelf was too high. She knew that, but she made several jumping grabs for her bag anyway. ''I'll just—be—a second,'' she explained between bounces.

''What are you doing?''

''I need my bag.''

''Why?'' He lifted a hand towel from a nearby rack.

She stopped her futile jumping and turned to him. ''Would you get my suitcase for me?'' she asked as pleasantly as she could.

He wiped away the remaining soap. ''What do you need it for?''

''Nothing that concerns you.'' She nodded toward the shelf. ''Please?''

His eyebrows dipping, he did as she asked, handing her the suitcase.

''Thanks.'' She breezed out without a second glance. Second glances where this man was concerned were dangerous.

She wasn't surprised when he followed her into her room. ''What are you going to do with it?'' he asked.

She tossed the case onto her bed, her pulse at life-threatening levels. Her ears rushed so loudly with blood she could hardly hear. Flipping the latches, she opened the bag. ''I'm running away with Stadler. He told me tonight he's breaking it off with Sareena, and he wants me back.'' She needed badly to look at his face, but she compelled herself to keep moving. She dashed over to her dresser and yanked out a drawer.

"You're *what*?''

She purposely spun away from him so that she couldn't be influenced by his body or his eyes. Without the slightest interest in what she was doing, she tossed the drawer's contents into her suitcase and closed it.

"Interesting trousseau,'' he muttered.

She jerked around to face him. "What?''

He crossed his arms before his broad chest, cocking his head toward her bag. "You just packed a drawer full of socks in that thing.''

She felt like a fool for being so oblivious, but she masked it by rearing her chin in defiance. "What are you doing in here anyway? This is none of your business.''

His expression darkened. "You're not serious about this.''

"Why not?'' she demanded, striving for an offhand tone. "You and I aren't married, so what does it matter?''

Everything about him went still, as though her query had broadsided him. After a few seconds, he ran a hand over his eyes. "My God, Lucy,'' he said, sounding troubled, "was that your plan all along? To make him jealous?''

That ploy hadn't occurred to her, but it would do for an excuse. She yanked up the suitcase. "It worked, didn't it?''

His eyes blazed with outrage, a staggering sight. Lucy's limbs reacted to it by going sluggish. She wished she'd had the self-control to keep her glance averted from his. With a shuddery intake of breath, she gathered strength and stormed by him. "Oh, and don't worry about your rings. They're in my jewelry box on the dresser.''

His answer was a muffled curse.

Now what are you going to do, big guy? her mind shouted as she flew up the stairs and dashed headlong for the parlor. She burst into the room, her determination formed like a rock inside her.

''Stadler,'' she called, then cleared the shrillness from her voice. ''I'm ready to run away with you, darling. Mind carrying my bag?''

Stadler's fair head popped up, his plum eyes going round with surprise. Clearly, he hadn't expected this, but he bounded over to her and took her bag.

Just then, amid gasps of surprise, Jack padded into the room, clad only in his towel and looking like an angry Greek god. ''You can't do this, Lucy,'' he growled.

''Of course I can.'' She grabbed Stadler's arm and aimed him for the door. ''You have your car keys, don't you, love? We can send for your things later.'' For once, Stadler seemed to be without words. Lucy felt a twinge of guilt at what she was doing. Then the memory of the letter he'd sent her—dumping her—flared in her mind, and she let her guilt go. ''Come, darling.'' She threw him a simpering smile. ''We've wasted enough time. I'm ready to start a new life tonight.''

When they hit the front porch, the frosty air slapped her, and she was reminded of the cold front that had swept in today, nipping the crocus and the redbuds. It was freezing, and she'd forgotten her coat. She fairly dragged Stadler down the steps toward his car, parked in the circle drive. She could tell from the clatter behind her that Jack wasn't the only person following them outside.

She peeked out of the corner of her eye. Everybody was on the porch but Jack. He was standing on the front lawn. So tall, so gorgeous in his near nudity, his expression was murderous. "Lucy, don't go," he shouted, but she ignored him, climbing into Stadler's rental compact.

Her companion fairly ran around to his door. He shoved her suitcase into the back and was in the driver's seat in a flash. "You won't regret this, Lucy-pet," he said, sounding short of breath.

"I hope not," she mumbled, looking in the side rearview mirror. Jack was framed there, legs braced wide, hands on hips. His features haunted. But he was no longer demanding that she stay.

She swallowed hard and prayed.

When Stadler turned the key in the ignition, she thought she heard something over the sound of the engine. As Stadler started to shift into gear, she touched his arm. "Just a second." She rolled down her window. "What?"

Jack dragged both hands through his wet hair. "I said you can't marry him. You're already married to me."

There it was! The truth. Her heart leaped, but her anger at his deception flared.

"What did he say?" Stadler asked, but she whipped around to him and held up a hand. "Shush!"

Then she glared back at Jack, accusing coldly, "I don't believe you."

He took several steps toward her, then stopped, holding out his hands in a pleading gesture. "I'm sorry. I didn't know how to tell you—but you're my wife."

He didn't know how to tell her?

"He didn't know how to..." Stadler sounded baffled. "Say, Lucy, didn't you know you were married?"

She whirled on him. "Would you please shut up for once?" Sticking her head out the window, she pretended amusement. "Jack, it's dear of you to keep pretending, but you can cut it out. I've told Stadler everything."

Jack's tortured gaze slid to the dark sky, and she saw his breath frost the night air in a long, unhappy sigh.

"It's okay, Jack," she added with effort. "It's better this way." Louder, she said, "Okay, Stadler, we can go."

"Dammit, Lucy, *stop*!" Jack called, his voice like an echo from a tomb. "You're married to *me*."

Stadler again reached for the key, but Lucy slapped his hand back. "Don't touch that!"

"But you said—"

"One more second." She shifted away from him and stared at Jack, the lift of her chin exhibiting defiance and subtle challenge. "You know, Jack, you actually sound serious."

"I've never been more serious in my life," he murmured. His features had grown watchful, brooding. The effect was heart wrenching, and she felt her chest constrict, but she fought to hold on to her resentment.

Fumbling for the door handle, she almost fell out of the car. After righting herself, she called over her shoulder, "Wait right *here*, Stadler." She slammed the door and faced Jack, glaring at him reproachfully. "What kind of a snake would marry a woman and not bother to tell her about it?" Her teeth chattered and her body quivered. She was freezing, but she planted herself there, crossing her arms and holding her silence. She wanted him to pay dearly for what he'd put her through.

His expression was like that of someone who'd been hit in the gut with a bat. She saw him shudder as he drew in a sharp breath.

His anguish touched her, and she felt another stabbing pain in her heart, but she tried to overlook it. "Well?" she demanded. "What kind of a lying *snake* would do such a thing?"

He closed his eyes, shaking his head. When he met her gaze again, Lucy saw bleak frustration and pain in his eyes, his vulnerability laid bare. ''A snake so blindly in love he couldn't help himself,'' he admitted in a rusty whisper.

His rough admission made her heart stumble. She didn't think she had ever heard anything quite so beautiful in her life. All the bitterness and anger left her, and she could only stare at the gorgeous, nearly nude man standing in the cold, saying the words she wanted so badly to hear.

''Lucy,'' Stadler called, ''what's going on?''

She ignored him. ''Why didn't you tell me, Jack?'' she asked, the hostility gone from her tone.

''I would have, when I thought you were ready.'' His chiseled features were stark. ''Nate called that night. He wanted to perform the wedding and I didn't have time to tell him the truth.'' A muscle flexed in his jaw. ''Then I heard about the myth.'' Dark, desolate eyes sought hers. ''Dammit, Lucy, I've loved you for so many years, I wanted to believe the myth was true. That we were meant for each other. So I let Nate marry us. For real.''

Unable to help herself, she moved toward him. ''You've loved me for years?''

When he nodded, she was overwhelmed with regret about the time they'd wasted and reflexively punched him in the stomach.

He grunted, his features pained. ''I deserved that.'' Placing his hands on her arms, he said, ''If you don't love me, you can get the marriage annulled. But—'' he stopped, seemingly to get control of his voice ''—I couldn't let you become a bigamist.''

''That's large of you.'' There was more testiness in her voice than she felt. He loved her. He'd loved her for years. That was all that mattered. Well, almost. The Desiree Question reared its ugly head. ''But before I get my annulment, there are some things we need to clear up.''

"Can we do it inside?" With a shudder, he added, "Or if you want to be rid of me quickly, we could argue out here a little longer and you'll become The Widow Gallagher."

She glared at him. "Wait here." Wheeling around, she marched to Stadler's car and stuck her head in the window. "Don't go anywhere. Okay?"

He nodded, but looked put out.

After stalking back to Jack, she took his hand. "Come on, mister. You have some explaining to do."

They marched up the steps as Elissa, Helen, Damien and four guests silently stepped back to clear their way.

"I can't wait to hear this story," Elissa said in an aside to Damien.

He laughed. "Amazingly enough, I can tell it—at least up to this point."

Lucy cast him a dubious look, and he winked. Confused, she tugged Jack along to her room. Once inside, she closed the door and turned on him. "Okay." She shoved hard against his chest, and he stumbled backward onto her bed. "Talk to me, Gallagher! And it had better be good!"

He lifted himself up on one elbow, looking steadily at her. "Shouldn't I get dressed?"

"No." She walked toward him. "Who exactly is Desiree?" He sat up, but she pushed him down, continuing to lean over him, her hands on his chest. Conjuring up the most severe expression in her arsenal, she said, "Answer the question."

He lay there, eyeing her warily. "If I tell you, you're going to punch me again."

She thought she detected a hint of humor in his gaze. "Don't you laugh at me, Jack Gallagher. Who is Desiree?"

His expression grew sheepish. "Okay," he said with a resigned breath. "Desiree is Damien."

She frowned, unsure she'd heard right. "Desiree is who?"

He grabbed her wrists as though in self-protection, just in case she decided to hit him. "Damien did the calling, pretending to be a fictitious woman named Desiree. Mainly, his end of the conversation consisted of, 'Jack, you're making me puke,' and 'You're scaring me, man.' Since he knows more French than I do, he fed me a few French phrases. Once I repeated them, he'd tell me they meant things like, 'The pig is eating slop,' or 'Smelly shoes belong on the back porch.'" He grinned, looking charming and guileless. "Damn bastard has a crappy sense of humor."

Scowling, Lucy climbed on the bed and straddled his waist. "Damien called you night and day, day and night, and pretended to be a French—" she choked back an inelegant word that came to mind "—*model*?"

"We thought a little jealousy might…" He stopped, letting her finish it in her mind.

Her mouth sagged open. "Did everybody know?"

He shook his head. "Only Damien. And he didn't know we were really married."

That was a relief, but not much of one. Irritated beyond words at the scheme, she tried to free a hand to punch him, but he held tight. "*You bum*!" she accused him. "That was—that was…" She didn't know slimy enough words to call him.

"Smart?" he teased.

"It was mean, deceitful, rotten!" She struggled unsuccessfully to free her hands to slap him silly.

"But you do know you love me now, right?"

She was taken aback by his blunt statement. How had he guessed? "Of course I *don't* love you now!" she blurted, indignant. "How could I love a man who—"

"Right." Jack slid his hands from her wrists to cup her hips. "How could you love me? How dare I force myself to move slowly because of your bruised feelings over your breakup with Stadler?'' The humor had left his gaze. ''How could you love me when I had the nerve to want to be sure you were over him, that you cared for me, before I acknowledged my love. You see, I didn't want your attraction to be nothing more than rebounding emotions or gratitude or revenge sex.'' His cinnamon eyes glistened, and the depth of feeling she witnessed there left her both humbled and enthralled.

She lost her urge to slap him as a delightful mix of desire and anticipation crept along her nerves. His caressing hands became erotic, hypnotic. Her fingers were no longer fisted, but spread, splayed over the warm expanse of his chest, relishing the crinkly feel of his chest hair.

''Lucy?'' His eyes shone with raw emotion. ''Before we were married, I told you one truth and one lie. The truth was, when I married, it would be forever. The lie, that our marriage was a farce. I had to wait and hope that one day your heart would embrace the truth over the lie.''

His silky words, his gentle caresses, at last convinced her beyond a doubt that she was truly loved. That his actions had been reckless, yes—but ultimately right.

Her heart soaring with happiness, she taunted him with a haughty look. ''Such conceit. What makes you think I don't *despise* you?''

He chuckled wickedly. ''A woman doesn't straddle a man she despises.'' One warm, questing hand slid up her back, drawing her face to his. ''Does she, darling?'' His lips moved over hers, branding them with his hot mastery.

Blood hammered in her brain, and she began to tremble. There was nothing more erotic, more magical, than the discovery of being loved.

She had a sudden, melancholy thought and drew

away, sighing. Jack's expression grew watchful. "What is it?"

"I was just thinking of Elissa."

His lips twitched ruefully. "Oh, fine. That says a lot for my lovemaking."

She smiled at him, then kissed him on the tip of his nose. "No, silly, I was thinking that she'll be all alone when I go away with you." Her fiery redheaded sister was really quite fragile in her own way, but she disguised it with her own brand of flippant toughness. Lucy knew in her heart that her big sister would be lonesome. But she would never let it show, hardhead that she was. "I hope she finds happiness." Lucy had an inspiration. "We'll just have to get her into the D'Amour mansion on her birthday under a full moon."

Jack's deep chuckle rippled through her body, sultry and sensual. "We'd have to tie her up and gag her, Luce. You know she doesn't believe in such things."

"But, Jack, don't you think—"

"I think," he interrupted, wrapping his arms around her and drawing her against him, "Elissa would be horrified to know we were discussing her right now." He kissed her deeply. "Lucy, I love you so much—the way you care about the people you love." He swept a wisp of her hair back, his loving smile, his gentle touch, making her weak with need. "Don't worry about Elissa, darling. She's one of the Crosby sisters, and that's a special gift some lucky man will discover one day." He lifted his head a fraction to kiss her shoulder, his eyes shining with purpose. "Now, let's talk about us...."

In a scandalously short time, Jack's gentle lovemaking, his sexy declarations, made her forget everything but the magnificent depth of his love for her.

Deep in the night, after Jack had become much, much more than a paper husband to Lucy, he whispered, "You told Stadler to wait."

With a throaty giggle, she slid across Jack's hips to perch intimately on top of him. She grinned, feeling wicked and wonderful. "It was a dirty trick, but if he gets cold, he can cover himself with my socks."

His grin made something inside her melt and begin to glow. What they'd found together tonight was so good. So right.

"Out there in the car with Stadler, you knew we were married, didn't you?" he prodded, looking charmingly suspicious. "You wanted me to suffer."

She smiled down at his face, loving the depth of emotion in his eyes. With a rush of womanly power, she moved against him, soft flesh brazenly taunting hard. "And are you suffering, darling?"

"Oh—yes...." His husky answer trailed over her like caressing fingers, and she quivered with a heady, sexual heat. "Oh, yes, my love," he repeated, his tone rough with urgent desire, "I'm suffering." He swept her to her back, drawing from her a happy cry. Lifting himself over her, his body captured hers in a web of worshipful stimulation. Deepening, intensifying, until, at last, they flew away once more to their private lovers' paradise.

The enchanted D'Amour mansion had once again worked its romantic magic. And Jack's lie—spoken out of love—was indeed the truth in masquerade.

*   *   *   *   *

*Watch the sparks fly when the mysterious owner
of the D'Amour mansion arrives on the scene,
and fiery Elissa Crosby finally meets her match.
Renee Roszel's* Enchanted Brides *trilogy comes
to an exciting close with Elissa's story.
Look out for this in late 1998.*

MILLS & BOON®

Next Month's Romances

♡

Each month you can choose from a wide variety of romance novels from Mills & Boon®. Below are the new titles to look out for next month from the Presents™ and Enchanted™ series.

Presents™

SINFUL PLEASURES	Anne Mather
THE RELUCTANT HUSBAND	Lynne Graham
THE NANNY AFFAIR	Robyn Donald
RUNAWAY FIANCÉE	Sally Wentworth
THE BRIDE'S SECRET	Helen Brooks
TEMPORARY PARENTS	Sara Wood
CONTRACT WIFE	Kay Thorpe
RED-HOT LOVER	Sarah Holland

Enchanted™

AN IDEAL WIFE	Betty Neels
DASH TO THE ALTAR	Ruth Jean Dale
JUST ANOTHER MIRACLE!	Caroline Anderson
ELOPING WITH EMMY	Liz Fielding
THE WEDDING TRAP	Eva Rutland
LAST CHANCE MARRIAGE	Rosemary Gibson
MAX'S PROPOSAL	Jane Donnelly
LONE STAR LOVIN'	Debbie Macomber

On sale from 6th April 1998

H1-9803

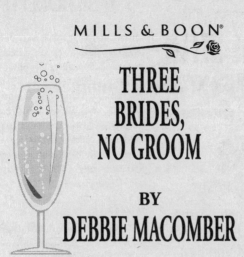

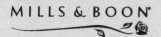

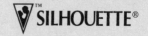

SPECIAL OFFER £5 OFF

FLYING FLOWERS

Beautiful fresh flowers, sent by 1st class post to any UK and Eire address.

We have teamed up with Flying Flowers, the UK's premier 'flowers by post' company, to offer you £5 off a choice of their two most popular bouquets the 18 mix (CAS) of 10 multihead and 8 luxury bloom Carnations and the 25 mix (CFG) of 15 luxury bloom Carnations, 10 Freesias and Gypsophila. All bouquets contain fresh flowers 'in bud', added greenery, bouquet wrap, flower food, care instructions, and personal message card. They are boxed, gift wrapped and sent by 1st class post.

To redeem £5 off a Flying Flowers bouquet, simply complete the application form below and send it with your cheque or postal order to; **HMB Flying Flowers Offer, The Jersey Flower Centre, Jersey JE1 5FF.**

ORDER FORM (Block capitals please) Valid for delivery anytime until 30th November 1998 MAB/0298/A

Title .... Initials .... Surname ....

Address ....

....Postcode ....

Signature...Are you a Reader Service Subscriber **YES/NO**

Bouquet(s) **18 CAS** (Usual Price £14.99) **£9.99** ☐   **25 CFG** (Usual Price £19.99) **£14.99** ☐

I enclose a cheque/postal order payable to Flying Flowers for £................................or payment by

VISA/MASTERCARD ☐☐☐☐☐☐☐☐☐☐☐☐☐☐☐☐ Expiry Date........../........../...........

PLEASE SEND MY BOUQUET TO ARRIVE BY........../........../.........

TO Title .... Initials .... Surname ....

Address ....

....Postcode ....

Message (Max 10 Words) ....

....

Please allow a minimum of four working days between receipt of order and 'required by date' for delivery.

You may be mailed with offers from other reputable companies as a result of this application. Please tick box if you would prefer not to receive such offers. ☐

Terms and Conditions Although dispatched by 1st class post to arrive by the required date the exact day of delivery cannot be guaranteed. Valid for delivery anytime until 30th November 1998. Maximum of 5 redemptions per household, photocopies of the voucher will be accepted.